POOK'S TENDER YEARS

One of the most rewarding aspects of a writer's work is to receive letters from readers asking for more information about his characters. Some requested details of Pook's early days, while others wanted to hear more about that fiery little nobleman, Honners.

In *Pook's Tender Years* Peter Pook has tried to satisfy both demands by drawing on the most amusing anecdotes of those formative years from eight to nineteen, and many of these stories are nearer the truth than he cares to admit—such as the de-railing of a tram with the aid of a kitchen poker and the destruction of his teacher's desk by force of gravity.

Also on record is Pook's first meeting with Honners at the Convent of the Holy Angels, where Honners was an unwilling martyr to religious rigours and where Pook's prayers were directed towards becoming a more proficient prizefighter.

Needless to say, in this book Pook begins his Tale of Woo, as he calls it, with his first love, Olga, and later as an enthusiastic gigolo working for the Rent-a-Gent Escort Bureau. The abundance of wit and humour to be found in *Pook's Tender Years* should satisfy all those readers who enjoyed the previous Pook Books so heartily, as well as attracting many new fans to the Pook brand of fast entertainment.

Peter Pook titles available from Emissary
(in the order in which they were originally published)

Banking on Form
Pook in Boots
Pook in Business
Pook Sahib
Bwana Pook
Professor Pook
Banker Pook Confesses
Pook at College
Pook's Tender Years
Pook and Partners
Playboy Pook
Pook's Class War
Pook's Tale of Woo
Pook's Eastern Promise
Beau Pook Proposes
Pook's Tours
The Teacher's Hand-Pook
Gigolo Pook
Pook's Love Nest
Pook's China Doll
Pook's Curiosity Shop
Marine Pook Esquire
Pook's Viking Virgins

POOK'S TENDER YEARS

Recalling his first childhood
before the onset of his second

PETER POOK

EMISSARY PUBLISHING
P.O. Box 33, Bicester, OX26 2BU, UK.
Tel: 01869 323447/322552   www.emissary-publishing.com

First published in Great Britain 1969
by Robert Hale Ltd., London.
Reprinted 1980

First published in paperback in 1993 by
Emissary Publishing, P.O. Box 33, Bicester, OX26 2BU, UK.
Reprinted 1998, 2002
New paperback edition published 2006
Reprinted 2012

www.emissary-publishing.com   www.peterpook.com
www.frederick-e-smith.com

British Library Cataloguing-in-Publication Data.
A catalogue record for this book is available from the British Library.

ISBN: 9781874490586

©Peter Pook 1969
Front Cover Illustration: Richie Perrott

Printed and bound by MWL Print Group Ltd., South Wales.

To all my readers
who asked for more Honners with their Pook

ONE

"Gampa Gampa, look out of der window, Gampa," the little boy lisped appealingly. "Gampa, Gampa, want to show you der pretty dododendem flowers, Gampa."

The wee eight-year-old in the garden squinted through his golden curls against the summer sun to the upper window which was his grandfather's room. Beside him was the pride of the garden, a beautiful rhododendron bush in bloom. It was indeed an idyllic picture of green lawn, multi-coloured flowers and the golden head of the child as he called so winsomely to the old gentleman above.

"Gampa, Gampa, open der window, Gampa," he lisped with the persistence of youth. "Look at der pretty dododendem flowers, Gampa. Peterkins want you to see der pretty dododendems Gampa." His arms held a scruffy ginger cat called Tibbles, a feline mixture of courage and cowardice who let himself be chased around the garden by the blackbirds who owned the land. The blackbirds had Tibbles just where they wanted him but Tibbles could be extremely brave when required, such as standing up to an earwig or holding his ground against the vicious attacks of a woodlouse. Of late he had taken upon himself the role of starling scarer. This hazardous task he accomplished by fearlessly rushing from cover just after the starlings had flown away, completing the sortie by leaping high into the air and flapping his forelegs like wings—always puzzled when he tumbled back to earth why he could not fly as these feathered cats did.

"Gampa, Gampa, open der window and let Peterkins show you the lubbly dododendems, please, Gampa. Dey do smell so boodiful, Gampa."

After twenty minutes the window slowly opened and a grisled face appeared, framed by a white beard so dear to the Victorians, who seemed to demand that a beard should not be merely decorative but also serve as a chest protector. Grandfather Pook was indeed an impressive sight, bald, broken-nosed, and so broad in the shoulders that they rested on each side of the window-frame.

"Oh, dere you are at last, Gampa. Peterkins calling you hours and hours to look out of der window, Gampa."

Grandfather yawned sleepily. "Well, here I am, Peterkins. What do you want then?"

"Want you to see der pretty dododendems, Gampa. Here, see."

"But I see them every day, Peterkins. What's so special about them this afternoon that you must wake me up from my forty winks? Don't tell me they need watering again—you nearly hosed them away this morning."

"Special dododendems today, Gampa. Watch carefully."

With an artless smile the little boy inserted his free hand in the bush, whereupon there came a sharp *platt* noise from the airgun fixed under the blossoms and suddenly Grandfather's face was full of spread potato, causing it to retreat angrily into the room.

The oaths that filled the neighbourhood brought Grandmother Pook running from the kitchen. "Come here at once, you obnoxious little guttersnipe, and I'll box your ears," she roared, rummaging among the rhododendrons for the airgun and breaking the cord holding it to a stake in the correct firing position for the bedroom window. "So this is where all my spuds have been disappearing to of late! Ammunition for your blasted airgun. It's a wonder you haven't knocked your poor Grandfather's eye out."

"Please don't break my nice new airgun, Gamma," the little boy pleaded, seeing it across her knee. "I was only doing what you told me."

"And what did I tell you?"

"You said Peterkins mustn't fire lead pellets at Gampa, so

I used potato instead because that's nice and safe."

"Break it I will—and you'll be the next object across my knee. And don't you dare call me Gamma, you snivelling little rat. You know damn well you can speak properly, and you only lisp that vile Gampa twaddle all day and half the night so that old fool upstairs will fall for your crafty ways and give you pocket-money all the time. Any more Gampa out of you, you wheedling little devil, and I'll horsewhip you within an inch of your wicked life."

Peter tried to pipe his eye but failed to squeeze out the timely tear. "Oh, please don't be cross, Gamma—it was only Peterkins' fun to make Gampa laugh when he's sleeping off the beer."

"Do you want to drive me out of my mind, lisping like an idiot and calling yourself Peterkins? Haven't I got enough trouble with the old man without you whining like a little halfwit? Just you put that cursed fire out in the shed, then go straight to bed. Look at it!—smoke pouring out of the door and window. No wonder the neighbours think there's a pyromaniac loose in the district."

Typical of most small boys, Peter found fire irresistible. In the shed at the bottom of the garden was an ancient brazier, and in this sooty container every scrap of combustible material had been consumed for the past week. In order to keep the fire going day and night, Peter had burned everything movable in the garden, including Grandfather's potting-out boxes and Grandmother's clothes-prop. By night he dragged in the old garden bench, to be broken up and fed to the flames. When Grandfather was forced to padlock the coal-shed, Peter turned his attention to the trellis-fence, until neighbours complained that everything made of wood in their gardens was mysteriously disappearing.

On Wednesday of that week Peter made an important discovery in the field of science—that lino burns fiercely, with a satisfying hissing sound like gas-jets. By Friday his bedroom contained no floor-covering, just bare boards. Mrs. Sopworth next door came in to inquire if a licensed crematorium had been established on our premises, and if so, would Mrs. Pook be so kind as to suspend ceremonies on Monday, the conventional washday. During that week Peter gradually changed into a coloured child as the heat and soot turned his rosy face a patchy shade of brown.

Peter loved his Grandfather as only a child can love an old man who spoiled him at every turn. He loved his Grandmother too, but with that reserve due to a woman who had been seeing through men for so long that she was partially psychic. They were caring for Peter while his father was abroad on one of those prewar naval commissions which were so long that they were like emigrating in uniform—so long that his mother emigrated too, in order to set up home in Hongkong rather than be an ocean widow back in England.

Peter didn't really mind being sent to bed early because he had an important job to start on the morrow—at dawn to be precise. His current hero was Harry Brett, the local milkman, who was the most wonderful person in the world performing the most wonderful job in the world. Peter had studied his every move for three weeks, following him round the houses noting the smallest traits of his character and the minutest details of his duties. Harry wore a cloth cap supported by special ears, each of which was nature's bracket for holding a pencil. The pencils recorded deliveries on a sheet secured between two wooden covers. Harry wore a dung-coloured coat, breeches with leggings, and he carried a pail of milk so heavy that over the years his legs had grown bandy, giving him the most fascinating gait Peter had ever seen. Hanging from a ledge inside the pail were two measures, pint and quart, for filling his customers' jugs.

Harry knew everything there was to be known about milk

and smelt delightfully of his stock-in-trade. In the street, Harry pushed a float surrounded by milk-cans, but dominating the float was an enormous churn with a tap for replenishing the pail. After every three calls Harry operated a plunger at the top of the churn to stir the cream thoroughly, thus ensuring the right mixture for everybody. Harry knew jokes, catch-phrases and songs about milk. He flirted with the maids, played with the youngsters, and distributed breath-taking snippets of local gossip—the most novel being the alleged connection between his milk and the customers' pregnancies.

But above all things Harry could yodel. Peter followed Harry right up Cudford Crescent as one in a trance, listening to the most beautiful sound in the world.

"Milk-O-lay-ettee! Milk-O-lay-ettee!" Harry cried at each house, and each time Peter chuckled and clapped his hands together as though the angels were singing to him direct from heaven.

Soon Harry's yodel developed a kind of shrill echo— "Milk-O-oo-de-tee! Milk-O-oo-de-tee!" as Peter followed him round and imitated his hero's cry in a squeaky treble each time it rippled round Cudford Crescent. Peter was the ideal audience for Harry, shrieking with delight at the traditional jokes of the trade, no matter how many times he had heard them before. Not only did he imitate Harry's yodel and mannerisms but also the bandy walk. He discovered that by following close behind Harry and bending the knees outwards he could copy the walk to perfection, even to the slight sway of the shoulders.

So it was that Peter abandoned his determination to become a dustman, replacing it with a burning resolve to be a milkman. Jim Neal, the dustman, now lost all glamour in Peter's eyes and he deserted him completely for the exotic world of milk. With that enviable propensity for adoption so typical of the young, Peter rapidly equipped himself for his new career, furnishing his wheelbarrow with a churn from what had previously been his Grandmother's boiling copper, complete with draining tap. A garden rake provided the stirring rod. The rest was simple; a pail for door-to-door deliveries, in which hung the two measures made from cocoa-tins. His tram-conductor's bag to hold the takings, paper fastened between a pair of table-mats to record them, Grandfather's cap on his head and Grandfather's pencils protruding above each ear.

The most difficult item of the rig had been the leggings. Peter cut these with great care from some of the bedroom lino he had not yet burned; fashioned them so cunningly that they were curved in approved bow-legged design, giving people the impression that his little legs were practically circular in shape. Already the churn was filled to capacity with the essential stock-in-trade of any would-be milkman—three gallons of whitewash, skilfully mixed in the burning shed. Peter was now fully organized and equipped to start up on his own and put Harry out of business.

Harry made two rounds a day, one at 7 a.m., the other at 3 p.m., so it was necessary for Peter to start at 6.30 a.m. Rising half an hour early, Peter carefully dressed for his new career, then, although it was nigh impossible to wake his grandparents apart from gunfire, he crept silently down to the shed for the float-cum-wheelbarrow. This was the heavy work, trundling the loaded barrow out into Cudford Crescent.

Next, he filled the pail from the churn, then bent his knees in the approved bandy gait and bobbed slowly along to his first customer.

"Milk-O! Milk-O-oo-de-tee! Milk-O-oo-de-tee!" Peter cried in the shrill falsetto of youth. Mrs Sopworth opened her back door and stared in wonder at the tiny figure shambling bowlegged towards her.

"Milk-O! Milk-O-oo-de-tee! Marnin' to 'e, mam. Lovely marnin' for cows. I've been up all night amilkin' of 'em for 'e, ma'am. Me wife's getting jealous but you comes first, ma'am."

Mrs Sopworth's hair-curlers shook with surprise at the apparition. "What on earth are you doing here at this hour, Peter? And what's wrong with your legs?—you look like an advanced case of rickets."

"I'm helping Harry with his round, ma'am," Peter lied with practised ease. "What would 'e be after havin' this marnin'—pint or cort?"

Too amazed to protest further, Mrs Sopworth ordered a quart.

"One cort of cow-juice coming up, ma'am," Peter replied in Harry's accent and style. Then he ladled a quart of whitewash into Mrs Sopworth's jug, adding a tiny drop more for good measure, just as he had seen Harry do. "That'll be sixpence to 'e, ma'am—a tanner to anyone else."

Dazedly, Mrs Sopworth handed the money to Peter, who entered it against her name on a form headed *Cudford United Football Sweep*. "What about cotted keem, ma'am? Want any Cornish cotted keem today, ma'am? That's the stuff to put you in the family way, ma'am."

"No thank you, Peter, no cream today. Now the milk has come I'll go inside and make myself a strong cup of tea. By the way, I shouldn't repeat that last remark to your customers, Peter—it's rather naughty, even when Harry says it."

Peter touched his big cap and shuffled off with the knees slightly bent, shoulders swaying, an odd little figure in dawn's early light.

"Milk-O! Milk-O-oo-de-tee!" Next door was Mrs Lowe, wife of Major Lowe, who kept a maid, Betty—one of Harry's favourites. When she opened the door Peter trilled the song he had heard so often from his hero's lips. "I love Betty, I saw her wink. I'm all right for a bit—I think!"

"Why, you cheeky young monkey, Peter—I'll tell your grandma about you," Betty protested.

"Pint or cort, Betty darlin'? I'm helping Harry with his round this marnin'."

"Oh, I see. A quart as usual, please."

"Cort o' liquid love for me darlin' coming up. And there's a wee extra drop o' babies' delight for 'e, my pretty. Any keem today, sweetheart? Any cotted Cornish keem that makes pretty maids want to squeeze me in their arms and kiss me wicked lips. It's the very essence of distilled love, me darlin' heart."

Betty grinned good-naturedly and ordered one carton. She received a carton of extra thick clotted whitewash, labelled Cudford Dairies' Rich Cream from our own Happy Cows.

"Thank you, Peter. Now master can have his tea nice and early. Bye-bye, love."

It was not until Peter was serving 27 Cudford Crescent that the first dissatisfied customer emerged from her house, waving a jug of whitewash in the direction of the new tradesman and informing the neighbourhood that she'd see the little devil in Borstal before she'd finished with him. Others followed suit, making it clear to all and sundry that tea or coffee made with whitewash wasn't doing anything for their stomachs, let alone their tempers. Major Lowe was reported to be regurgitating at regular intervals, while Mrs Sopworth's husband was obviously unfit for work, being in the throes of a lacteal allergy of some violence, and there was general support for a proposal to send for a stomach-pump from Cudford Hospital.

Repercussions followed swiftly. All moneys paid by the residents for whitewash were refunded by Mrs Pook, who apologized on behalf of Peter and forbade his further participation in the milk trade on pain of flogging. Moreover, Peter had to apologize to Harry for his unfair business methods and promise his Grandmother that never again would he walk bow-legged or retail whitewash for any purpose whatsoever.

While Peter was in bed, trying to fathom where his scheme went wrong, his grandparents held a private conference together downstairs. The outcome of their deliberations was twofold.

First, it was decided that Peter needed a hobby, and, second, that his Grandfather was the best qualified person to provide him with one. The dear old couple little suspected that, could they but see into the future, it would have been wiser to let well alone and let him play at the comparatively harmless game of Milk-O.

Like all the books in my Grandfather's small library— which reposed in a chest under his bed—the three slim volumes had no covers. In fact, for years I imagined the old man ripped the cover off every book he bought to save space in his box. The three tattered little publications he presented to me on my birthday bore the intriguing titles of *Boxing,* by Jem Mace, *The Noble Art of Self-Defence,* by Ned Donnelly, and *Pedestrianism,* by Anonymous.

"Read these carefully, Peterkins, then I'll teach you the noble art of self-defence," Grandfather told me shortly after the milk disaster. "Every boy should know how to look after himself, then you won't ever get bullied at school."

Grandfather's words impressed me deeply because not only had he met and defeated every prize-fighter of the nineteenth century but also remembered talking to the mighty champions of the eighteenth century. More recently he had been on intimate terms with the fighting fraternity of the twentieth century, but how one man managed to span three centuries I never discovered. Even so, the three instruction manuals—which lie before me as I write—were produced around the 1870's, with the result that I unwittingly followed methods a little out of date, to say the least. For example, Ned Donnelly added a footnote to his work stating that 'Should any of my definitions with pencil or with pen seem to require further elucidation, I shall be happy to demonstrate in person to any pupil all and any of the glories of our art. To use an old sporting phrase, I am still to be heard of at Mr Waite's well-known school of arms,19, Brewer Street, Golden Square, London W., where I give lessons, and where I may be seen any day between ten and six.'

Owing to the nature of the woodcuts in Mr Donnelly's manual of exercise I adopted the stance of the old-time prize-fighters—legs wide apart, knees bent, both fists held extremely high, as though the main danger of attack might well come from an adversary who descended from the sky like a paratrooper. I was anxious to consult Mr Donnelly personally on this question of the high guard, for I fondly imagined him leaning by the door of 19, Brewer Street, dressed in the recommended elastic vest and cotton drawers, his mighty arms folded beneath those waxed moustachios, waiting for novices like me to seek his advice. Whenever I suggested a trip to London for this purpose Grandfather always gave the same reply. "We mustn't bother Ned just now, Peterkins. I know him well and he's a very busy man at the moment. We'll call on him some other time."

Even today I still have that nostalgic feeling that a visit to Mr Waite's well-known school of arms in Golden Square would enable me to meet the old champion any day between ten and six, when he would bow gracefully and demonstrate how his tremendous upper-cut could lift you clean out of Brewer Street. Once, Grandfather suggested that when we did eventually visit London to consult Ned, we should also call upon Gentleman Jackson's school of boxing in Bond Street, fashionable haunt of the Regency bucks. As Gentleman Jackson opened this establishment in 1795, I was extremely curious to meet such an aged practitioner of the noble art, and longed to hear Grandfather talking to him about Jack Dempsey, whom Grandfather had fought as recently as 1920.

I read the little books and studied the woodcuts by the hour, until I had them off pretty well by heart. I learned that the Noble Art of Self-Defence was really a euphemism for the

Savage Art of Self-Destruction, with the result that I was won over to the sport completely. Pleased with my interest in the fight game, Grandfather presented me with another coverless book for my off-duty reading, *Fights of the Fancy.* Night after night in bed I read with dilated eyeballs and sweating forehead the eye-witness accounts of every bare-knuckle encounter, from eighteenth-century James Broughton and Jack Slack to Tom Sayers in 1860, so that often I did not so much fall asleep on my pillow as drop unconscious in my corner. Once I had survived the accompanying nightmares induced by the welter of blood involved in my new career, I decided that this was life as it should be lived, and henceforth I determined to be a pugilist.

Imagine my surprise when, at the very first lesson from Grandfather, he produced a set of gloves. "We don't need those, Grandpa," I protested. "Tom Cribb and Daniel Mendoza never fought with gloves on."

"Must be done, Peterkins. You can only fight bare-fisted if you harden up the hands by pickling them in brine, and, I'm sorry to say, Grandma has definitely forbidden that."

It was many a day before I forgave Grandmother for her cruel decision, though she little knew that I now read *Fights of the Fancy* at nights with my little hands immersed in a bowl of brine.

Grandpa laced the six-ounce gloves on my fists for the first lesson, how to stand. Either my stance was incorrect or one was supposed to stand flat on one's back, because Grandpa's initial left lifted me clean off my feet. "That's to teach you to stand properly," he explained incongruously, drying my eyes for me. "Keep your feet eighteen inches apart and move easily on your toes."

Grandfather shadow-boxed with me for several minutes until I had mastered the art of standing upright, then he said, "Now, here's your first trick of the trade. Spar with your opponent, thus, till you catch his eye with your own; then look to your right and lead with your left as he follows your glance, so."

Once again I lay flat on the lawn, visible proof of the trick's efficacy. "That's a jolly clever trick, Gampa," I gasped admiringly when I had recovered my wits, "Now let me try it on you."

We sparred until I caught his eye staring straight into mine, then I looked to the right as instructed and kicked Grandpa in the groin with my left boot.

Even by today's standards the language flying about our garden is unprintable, as Grandfather proceeded to demonstrate the true meaning of the noble art of self-defence. Perhaps he had in mind that delightful old Queensberry Rule which states that 'A contestant hanging over the ropes in a helpless state with both toes off the ground, shall be deemed to be down and entitled to a count of ten.' I learned a great deal in that first lesson: because, as Grandfather put it while staunching the blood from my face, "You got that hiding to teach you to fight fair and not lose your temper in the ring, you vicious little squirt."

"But you lost your temper too, Gampa, just because I invented my very own trick," I blubbered.

"I'll really lose it if you don't stop piping your eye. Now dry up and start the footwork and straight left together."

Every day I worked out with Grandfather in the garden, and when he tired I beat my little fists against the punch-bag he rigged up for me, hanging from a branch of Mrs Sopworth's tree which protruded over our wall. Mrs Sopworth didn't mind this but the platform ball Grandfather fixed to the blank wall of her house nearly drove her off her rocker. I learned to pound this at high speed, sending the reverberations through our neighbour's house like a pneumatic-drill, until so much pebbledash came loose from the building that the platform ball was banned.

Being a child of extreme thoroughness in all I undertook, I

read the training chapters of the manuals with zeal, endeavouring to follow their orders as closely as possible. Although writing around 1870, the author made the surprising statement that, compared with the old timers, the athletes of the day were soft, flabby, overweight, badly trained layabouts of poor colour, barely capable of even a mere sixty rounds. In sharp contrast, the pugilist of yore had been notable for the tightness of his skin and the ruddy colour underneath. Moreover, the fighter of 1870 was a disgrace to his profession, lacking the indomitable courage of his predecessors, being craven enough to throw in the sponge after only three hours of combat—'Truly this is the age of shams; shall I say an emasculated age, when science and bottom are subservient to flashy, tricky sparring?' A return to our former glories could only be obtained by purging, cold baths, sweats, clean living, and rubbing the face with lemon to roughen the skin. Before retiring at night the patient was to take antibilious pills, followed by senna-pods at daybreak. Then he jumped out of bed for the first seven-mile run of the day in sweaters.

Returning home, he was rubbed down with coarse towelling, then plunged into alternate hot and cold baths. Now, we are surprised to learn, he was ready for breakfast —steak, beer and port wine. The day being well advanced—past 6 a.m. in fact—it was time to start the real programme of the training camp.

I felt very keen to consult Ned Donnelly about the rigorous purging essential for success in the ring because my first purge resulted in my rolling about the bed in pain, more ready to die than fight. It was a complete mystery to me how such a drastic method could possibly help me as a boxer, reducing me to the position where I couldn't even stand on my two feet unless supported between my grandparents like a dying soldier, at the very moment when I was supposed to go out and fight to the bitter end. Grandmother found a packet of Epsom salts on my bedside table, so she let me spend the rest of the day groaning in the toilet, a pale shadow of the Cudford Infant, as I now styled myself in the best traditions of Fistiana.

My faith in the modest author of *Pedestrianism* diminished each time I followed his advice on how to get fit for battle, making me wonder if he was trying to lure me to an early grave. A week later, my Grandmother found me at seven in the morning, lying drunk on the kitchen floor, full of steak and Sandemans Port, and once again Grandfather had to carry the Cudford Infant to bed, where I slept motionless for eighteen hours. When I finally regained consciousness Grandfather told me, "Boxing's a dangerous game, Peterkins, and many men get hurt in the ring—but you're the first fighter I ever knew who took so much punishment without so much as donning a glove."

Whilst in bed I decided to dispense with purging and port wine for breakfast in order to concentrate on the seven-mile run. I set out from Cudford at 6 a.m., heading due north, as fast as my little legs could carry me, until I had run three hundred yards, when I was forced to jog-trot the next mile. The final six miles I walked, arriving at the village of Dorley in the early afternoon on my hands and knees, with the horrible sensation that my stomach had dropped out en route. I lay unashamedly on the pavement outside *The Travellers Joy,* wondering if a doctor would find me before I died in the gutter. They tell me a customer carried me into the inn while the landlord's wife revived me with brandy and her husband phoned the police, under the impression that I had been knocked down by a hit-and-run driver. This time I spent four days in bed, not so much through physical exhaustion as to allow my legs a chance to function again for the purpose of supporting my body. For the first time I realized why, throughout the pages of *Pedestrianism,* the athlete in training was referred to as the patient.

In a last effort to adhere to the ancient manual I determined to harden my body by means of the hot and cold baths. This I achieved by soaking in the bath as hot as one could bear, then running naked downstairs and jumping in our water-butt in the garden. The shock was so terrible that my screams filled the neighbourhood, which was just as well, seeing that my limbs were too numb to get me out of the butt again, because Mr Sopworth had the presence of mind to leap over the fence and pull me out before I drowned. Distinctly puzzled at finding a naked child in a water-butt at dawn, Mr Sopworth carried my shivering body indoors, where he had the embarrassing task of waking up my grandparents, then explaining to them that just as he was departing for work a splash and a scream brought him over the fence to make his mystifying discovery. Nor could he fathom the connection between my taking a bath upstairs and ending in the water-butt as though I had shot through the drain-pipe, except by concluding that I was a maladjusted child bent on suicide. My grandparents expressly forbade any more attempts to get fit especially as I was now bedridden with such a cold that my red eyes could scarcely see to read the print of *Fights of the Fancy.*

At this stage in my career as a pugilist my favourite sparring partner was Nancy Sopworth, our neighbour's little daughter. I secretly despised Nancy because it was obvious she would never reach the heights of her new profession, being prone to slap with the gloves rather than deliver crisp knuckle punches such as she received from me. Furthermore, she cried easily and lost her temper before a round was over, making her an easy prey to my counter-attacks. Much more formidable opposition came from Mrs Sopworth, who revealed an extra-ordinarily powerful right-hander round the ear to emphasize her ban on Nancy's further participation in my training.

Consequently I had to fall back on Betty, Major Lowe's maid. Betty was a stocky ginger-haired wench, possessed of a lovely left which she delighted to prod into my features at the most unexpected moments, such as when I was consulting the watch to see if three minutes were up.

"You wouldn't do that to me if I was as big as Harry," I used to moan unsportingly when the sparks before my eyes had subsided.

"'No, love, don't expect I would—but we could have a lovely kiss and cuddle together instead. Come and dry your eyes on my apron, then we'll have one more round for the championship of the world before tea."

I began to suspect that sparring with Betty might result in my nose disappearing from my face altogether, so I looked around for adversaries of my own age and sex. To this end I founded The Cudford Junior School of Arms—an association of remarkably short existence. Originally over twenty members enrolled, but as my garden quickly transformed from a school of arms to a slaughterhouse of howling kids, most members withdrew either through injury or by being marched home by outraged parents who were not prepared to see their gentlemanly sons turned into street ruffians overnight. After three weeks only Henry Pearce, the Game Chicken, and James King, the Liddale Assassin, remained in the school of arms.

It was not surprising that the Game Chicken should have earned his name as a direct result of his immortal fight with the Liddale Assassin in an eliminating contest for the Junior Flea-Weight Championship of the World—a bout which taught the Game Chicken just why the Liddale Assassin was so called. Following this massacre, badly aligned posters in crayon displayed in Cudford Crescent informed all sporting patrons that they were shortly to witness the final for the championship between the Cudford Infant and the Liddale Assassin, at the extremely reasonable price of one penny for a ringside seat. In fact, such patrons were destined to enjoy a restricted bill of entertainment from now on because our tournaments had to be permuted from the residue members of the school of arms. Thus the Cudford Infant fought the Game Chicken, with the Liddale Assassin as referee, so the main supporting contest had to be the Game Chicken versus the Liddale Assassin, refereed by the Cudford Infant. Therefore it was quite obvious that the only new contest we could offer the fans was the Liddale Assassin versus the Cudford Infant, refereed by that celebrated glutton for punishment, the Game Chicken.

Despite a record gate of three shillings, the contest for the Junior Flea-Weight Championship of the World reduced our membership to one, the Liddale Assassin resigning from our ranks because the decision went against him, and the Game Chicken being expelled from the club and deprived of his referee's licence for declaring the verdict a draw in the first place, thus proving beyond doubt that he had been got at by Monty Fairbanks, the rich boy of the district, who had thrilled the fans with an unheard-of wager—five shillings or his little sister— against my winning.

I found it extremely difficult to run a school of arms with a membership of one, so it had to be disbanded, but as I was involved in the case of the Cudford Tramways at this time I was not unduly distressed.

TWO

Returning to England on a short leave, my parents decided it was time they placed me in a school for young gentlemen before the authorities put me in a school for young felons. The trouble arose through my desire to help Cudford Tramways in a manner far outside their normal requirements. I had noticed that Tram 5 ran along Cudford Crescent until, with a satisfying rattle of points, it passed out of sight on its journey to the town centre. This happened four times an hour, but twice an hour came Tram 6 bound for the town's outskirts. At the points, Tram 6 had to stop, whereupon the heavily-clad driver hoisted out a kind of oar with an iron head, leaned over his brake-wheel, and dexterously changed the points without leaving the vehicle. Tram 6 was then able to proceed round the curve of rail and head for the suburbs.

I learned by experiment that one did not necessarily need an oar to change the points because, provided one was on foot, they moved quite satisfactorily with the aid of our kitchen poker. This discovery pleased me immensely, for now I was in a position to help the overworked drivers of Tram 6 by changing the points for them, thus saving time and improving relations between Cudford Transport Board and the general public.

Rather than bring official approval on my head I modestly concealed the poker up my sleeve and waited inconspicuously inside a phone booth for Tram 5. On the rail lay a halfpenny piece, placed there by me in the optimistic belief that, in order to reward me for my services, Tram 5 would flatten it to the correct size for fitting our local cigarette machine.

On the hour Tram 5 bowled along with that fascinating itch-and-yaw motion of short wheel-base vehicles, flattened the halfpenny beyond the capacity of any cigarette machine to accept, and disappeared southwards. In anticipation of Tram 6, I skilfully switched the points across, then retired to the privacy of the phone booth. After ten minutes' wait I was rewarded by the sound of a tram approaching from the northern end of Cudford Crescent, but when I read the number I ran panic-stricken from the booth, waving my arms for the driver of Tram 5 to stop. The driver glared at me and made familiar public transport signs awarded to would-be passengers who try to stop vehicles anywhere but at authorized halts. He then appeared to vacate his seat as if by magic, as Tram 5 suddenly departed from its normal course and veered round the curved rail with squeaks of help arising from flanged wheels grinding against the steel track.

I closed my eyes as if about to faint as Tram 5 gave up the struggle to remain Tram 5 instead of Tram 6, left the rails and jolted over the cobbles with a rotating overhead pulley-arm bobbing wildly to the sky. When I opened my eyes Tram 5 stood where no tram of any number had ever stood before— in the Japanese Tea-Garden of Mrs Worrall's combined cake shop and dainty teas parlour. Apparently the Japanese favoured extremely small gardens because the front end of Tram 5 had no option but to obtrude into the foreground of Cudford War Memorial.

Characteristically, I decided to make a clean breast of the unhappy affair, a decision in no way influenced by the driver being able not only to identify me but also to name me, and Constable Barrington finding a poker and a flattened halfpenny on my person. This frank admission, plus the fact that by some miracle nobody had been hurt or much damage caused, enabled the magistrate to discharge me with a caution and decided my father that the time had come to invoke that salutary treatment of the young so dear to British parenthood —the boarding school.

Ever solicitous for my welfare, father asked me what type of school I would prefer to pass the years nine to eleven in prior to entering either Grammar School or Borstal.

"Please, daddy, Peterkins would like to go to a school of arms," I lisped engagingly, giving him the Bubbles smirk and resting my curls artlessly on his lap in filial trust.

"What the devil is a school of arms?—Sandhurst?"

"No, daddy dear, it's a special place where they teach you the noble art."

"The noble art of what?—juvenile hypocrisy?"

"Sorry, daddy, Peterkins doesn't know what hypoxidy means, but it's a kind of academy where they show you how to defend yourself."

"So you won't need a lawyer, I presume. No, no, my lad, your boxing days are over. Have you ever heard of a boarding school?"

"Is that a posh name for a boxing school, daddy?"

"No, it is not. A boarding school is one where you live in during the term so that there may be some chance of your becoming a young gentleman rather than a fairground pug— and it costs plenty."

I bent my features for tears and made sobbing noises. "I don't want to be a burden on the family, daddy, because you always tell me you're hard up. I'd much rather go to a cheap boxing school. . . . "

"Your mother and I prefer a boarding school—and that's where you're going, so stop trying to weep like a normal child. Now, before we take you there handcuffed, we'd better soften the blow by buying you something really nice for your birthday. What would you like?"

"Oh, thank you, daddy dear! What I want above everything at the moment is a gum-shield."

"What on earth for?"

"Why, to protect my toofy-pegs when I fight, of course, daddy. You wouldn't want Peterkins to lose his nice new toofy-pegs, now would you, daddy? Why, there wouldn't be anything to clean before beddy-byes, and I might starve through not being able to chew my nice din-din. . . ."

"Shut up that nauseating drivel you should have forgotten when you fell out of the pram. You'll get a Meccano set like normal boys have."

Father enrolled me at the Convent of the Holy Angels, Brinton, which claimed to train children for the best public schools in the land. It was a splendid institution in every way, and I little knew how fortunate I was to be there, any more than the school realized how ill-advised it had been to admit me.

At the appointed hour my father presented me to Reverend Mother Blake, a lady of infinite wisdom and patience who might well have been, both in looks and demeanour, one of the holy angels referred to in the title of the school. She stared so long at my puffed face and closed eye that my father thought some explanation was called for. "Peter has been studying the noble art of self-defence, ma'am."

"Judging by appearances, he doesn't seem to have learned the art very well. One can only suppose that he has been instructed to defend himself with his face. What is wrong with his huge mouth, may one ask? Hasn't he any teeth?"

"Nothing amiss that I am aware of, ma'am. Peter, smile nicely and show Reverend Mother your mouth properly."

I smiled dutifully, to reveal the hideous white gum-shield I had purchased secretly with the money I wheedled out of Grandfather. Reverend Mother Blake started back in revulsion at my shark-like grimace, while father hurriedly ripped the thing from my mouth.

"Never mind, Mr Pook, we have several sweet little girls here who will exert a good influence on this, er, boy and smooth off the rough edges. You may leave him in our hands with every confidence."

I bade farewell to my father and followed Reverend Mother Blake through the great corridors of the convent to meet the other children. There were some sixty pupils all told, roughly divided into boys and girls. I was appalled to see the girls—they looked so angelic and pretty that momentarily I wondered if I had succumbed to measles and entered Heaven. One little girl in a frilly white dress came forward and said, "Who are you, boy?"

"I'm Peter Pook, the Cudford Infant," I retorted sourly.

"I'm 'Lithabeth."

"That's a funny name. I've never heard a girl called Lithabeth before."

"Don't you dare make fun of my lithp, you nathty boy."

"I didn't even know you had a lithp."

"Ith not half so funny ath your fathe."

"What's wrong with being Church of England then?"

"You horrid little boy—I mean your fathe, not your faith."

"Have it your own way, Lithabeth."

"I don't like you and I never thall, so there. You than't have any of my birthday caketh."

"What's birthday caketh, Lithabeth?"

"You're ugly and rude, thath what you are."

Time to shut this one up, I thought to myself, turning away for a second. Then I gave Lithabeth my horror face with the gum-shield. This made her scream with terror, and her tears brought Mother Delaney hurrying across to pacify her and lead me over to the boys' table for the evening meal. This consisted of cold pie, cheese and unlimited bread-and-butter, washed down with cocoa, which I devoured voraciously. Next to me was the smallest boy I had ever seen. He had auburn hair, big ears, an extremely determined chin but no nose. Nature had remedied this deficiency by supplying a red button.

"Hallo, light-bulb," I greeted him cheerfully. "Why don't you switch it off in the daytime?"

My new friend continued to bolt the victuals ravenously.

"Switch what off?" he demanded between swallows.

"Your little red nose, of course. No point in wasting the battery when there's no traffic about."

The little face coloured beetroot with indignation as he turned to the other boys. "Excuse my pig—he's a friend," he told them before looking at me. "You cheeky guttersnipe! I'll have you know I'm the Hon. Lesley Pilkington-Goldberg, 10th Earl Apparent, of Cudford Hall. You will call me sir. My friends call me Honners for short."

"That's a good name in your case—Honners for short. What would they call you if you weren't so short?"

The wedge of pie hit me right between the eyes, and everybody laughed delightedly. Mother Phelan stopped reading Gentle Children Softly Slumber aloud from the dais and hurried over to pull Honners off me by his hair, then several bigger boys sat on Honners before he overturned the table in rage.

"As you are a new pupil I shall not punish you this time, Peter," Mother Phelan told me severely. "However, Honners should know by now that young gentlemen do not greet newcomers by slapping pie in their faces and losing his temper once again. He shall do Litany tonight."

"Who is she, mummy?" I inquired puzzledly.

"Litany is not a she but an it Peter, and soon you will be doing it yourself. Moreover, I am fortunately not your mummy so you will address me as Mother Phelan in future—do I make myself clear?"

"Blast it!" Honners swore under his breath. "I seem to be on Litany every night of the year. You'll pay for this, Pook."

"Come, children, time for bed everyone—there's the bell."

"And don't we need it, what with getting up at dawn each day for Mass, then going to service every time that cracked muffin bell clangs," Honners moaned, hopelessly. I want to grow up and be a belted earl, not the next Pope."

The other boys showed me the way to our dormitory, a

large room containing some thirty beds on the lines of a hospital ward. My bed was next to Honners' but while the rest of us undressed it was his duty to read the Litany. In fact, whatever we did during the day was invariably accompanied by someone reading aloud something which had no connection with the task on hand, as though they were determined to take our minds off our work at all costs. For example, later on when we were doing practical work by constructing a simple brick wall, one of us was appointed to read aloud about the fall of Jericho.

Honners intoned the words of the Litany as though he was extremely cross with God, while the other boys chanted the responses. I felt quite out of things, not knowing the responses, so I gave up trying to undress in order to learn what my school-fellows were saying with such mechanical precision. As Honners passed me he hissed, "For St. Brinton's sake undress and hop into bed. I'm not allowed to stop warbling till everybody is ready to sleep, so I don't want to be up half the night waiting for you to realize that even in this sweat-shop day must have an end—we're called again at cockcrow and rushed unconscious into chapel to let God know we're not idling our lives away in bed at night like normal human beings do. Sometimes we're on Midnight Mass as well, so it beats me why we don't just park our beds in the nave and have done with it."

"But I don't know the responses to the Litany."

"Then don't respond—you'll end up in Hell anyway. Just kip down and shut up before I pass out on my feet."

I stared at Honners' feet in wonderment because attached to each was a small felt mat which slithered along the floor as he paced the dormitory. "Can't your folks afford to buy you slippers?" I asked.

"No one is allowed to interrupt the Litany, Pook, but for your information these are pedentes or floor-polishers. You'll soon learn in this religious Dartmoor that you're supposed to be a kind of human octopus, doing umpteen jobs at once. Thus I not only ruin my voice bellowing the Litany to keep our minds off our plight but polish the deck at the same time. You will notice that my right hand holds a rosary to count the responses, while my left hand carries the official cloth for dusting the oak panelling as I shuffle round the walls. If I wasn't so blasted short they'd probably tie a distemper brush on my head for the ceilings. The result is that visitors slip all over the place and break their legs as though we're billeted on an ice-rink. What beats me is why they don't give some employment to my idle knee-caps, such as squeezing lemons for breakfast."

"No talking there, Litany man," cried the Captain of the dormitory. "Keep chanting and polishing till lights out."

"That's Melhuish, our Captain of kip," Honners grunted as he slithered off. "I think he's studying to be a warder on Devil's Island."

Before we finally went to sleep Mother Phelan came in to take prayers, which was the signal for everybody to get up and kneel by their beds. I couldn't help noticing that Honners prayed in this position with a soft snoring sound. After general prayers Mother Phelan told us to recite our private prayers while she inspected the dormitory, and once again I marvelled at Honners' ability to perform this spiritual function like an advert for chloroform.

"And what are you praying for on your first night in your new home, Peter?" Mother Phelan whispered in my ear.

"I'm praying that I shall soon be back in my old home, Mother Phelan, and also I'm asking God to strengthen my right hand."

"What lovely Biblical language, Peter. As the Psalm tells us, 'Sit thou at my right hand, until I make thine enemies thy footstool.' Is that the passage you had in mind?"

"I don't think so, Mother. Being left-handed I can't punch so hard with my right, so I ask God every night to give me an auctioneer."

"Dear me! And what may this auctioneer be that you desire so much?"

"'That's Fistiana for a sleeping-pill in your mitt, Mother. I only hope God knows more about boxing than you do."

"It seems you and I will soon be due for a private talk about the proper use of prayer, young man. Until then, I bid you good-night. Very well, Honners, you may wake up now and get into bed, ready for lights out."

I could hear Honners cursing and swearing to himself as he undressed, in a manner most unsuitable for one who had previously been chanting the Litany. "Here I am, scion of one of the greatest families in the land, reduced to a blasted unpaid padre-cum-charwoman in this theological workhouse for the innocent. They'll have me hoovering the carpets next while I clean my teeth. How can they afford to let me lie idling the night away on this padded plank we use instead of a bed till nearly daybreak? Why can't I walk in my sleep on a treadmill and grind our daily bread. . . ?"

"Silence, that end of the dormitory. Light's out now but be ready for first angelus."

"Don't forget Midnight Mass—it helps break up the long night for us."

"Silence, Honners, or you'll find yourself on gardening fatigue tomorrow."

"So now they want me to dig my own grave. . . ."

"Report for gardening fatigue directly after morning ablutions, Honners."

"'Must be Harvest Festival already."

"And kitchen fatigue before Benediction."

"How does a poor devil transfer to the Free Church?"

Despite the arduous routine and frequent chapel attendance,

we received an excellent education whether we wanted one or not. The boys generally did not like mixing with the girls, but this integration had to take place at dancing class, where we learned the basic steps in the dances of the day. Honners had a devoted partner in Elizabeth, while I found myself clumsily jerking round the floor in the competent arms of Daphne Coombe. I remember holding Daphne by her frilly tulle dress and thinking how pretty she was for a girl. She was one of those precocious children who have acquired all the perfections of womanhood by the age of ten.

"Come along, Peter, copy me and you will be quite all right. Don't be shy—everybody falls over their feet to begin with —just follow the music and go in the direction I lead you."

I had not yet learned that the male partner leads, so I did my best to hop backwards in time to the music of the record.

"You dance beautifully, Daphne," I ventured when we had synchronized our hops so that we were able to travel like a pair of Siamese frogs.

"Thank you, Peter. I think I am going to like you better than Raymond Zimmerman. He always wants to lead, and I hate going backwards."

"Do you box too, Daphne?" I threw this question at everybody I met because the noble art was not listed on the curriculum at the Convent of the Holy Angels, and Reverend Mother Blake had informed me in no uncertain terms that it wasn't ever going to be, either. So far, Honners was the sole volunteer, but he was too small for my training schedule.

"Do I box, Peter? What a dreadful question to ask a young lady, though I might box your ears if you tread on my toes again. Better if you asked Raymond Zimmerman—he's a boy and ever so strong. He's sitting out this dance over there."

I glanced over Daphne's large hair bow she wore as though she intended rising in the air at any moment, like a helicopter. I found myself looking into the hostile eyes of Raymond

35

Zimmerman, heir to the mighty Zenith banking house but now unaccustomed wallflower and spectator of the dance.

Raymond returned my gaze by poking out his tongue at me and calling, "First time I've ever seen a kangaroo leaping backwards."

Here, I thought to myself, was someone I might be boxing quite soon. My reverie was broken by the sight of Honners, back from garden fatigue, dancing with little Elizabeth. Honners had solved the problem of the waltz by walking with short sharp steps all over the room with the speed of an early movie, like a blackbird who has lost its sense of direction. His wee head poked out from an Eton collar nearly as wide as his shoulders. Employing Elizabeth as a shield, he rammed into couples everywhere he went, muttering, "Dance, they tell you! Learn the social graces and dance! What they don't tell you is how you're supposed to have enough energy left to walk on all fours, let alone prance about the music room like a performing flea after you've dug up half Cudfordshire with a broken fork. No wonder we're in church day and night praying for strength. If ever I get out of this place alive I'm going down the salt mines for a rest. I can see it on the headstone now: 'After a long and arduous life of toil patiently borne, he passed peacefully away on his hoe at the advanced age of twelve. Erected to his memory by his sorrowing murderers.' Even then I expect they'll put a duster and a tin of furniture polish in the coffin just in case. How do they expect me to grow if I'm never in bed long enough to drop off? I bet God is proper fed up with our lot—we never give him any rest. Only last week they had me in church half the night, singing and praying my head off for peace. Well, I had peace all right till they woke me up and dragged me out of bed to pray for it. Then I happened to drop off and snore quietly in the pew, so Father Norman shook me awake to sing *Grant Us Blissful Slumber* with the choir. I told him to his face that it'd be more to the point if we sang *Grant Us Blissful Insomnia*."

"What's biting you now, Honners?" I asked, when my route with Daphne brought us near Honners by sheer coincidence.

Honners grimaced. "Surely you can see I'm heading for the infirmary, the way they're driving me, Peter. I'm just about good for one more banana season, so save up for the wreath. It beats me why they don't use the whip while we're prancing about in here to learn deportment or whatever they call dying on your feet. What good will the social graces be to me if I have to bow and simper to society from a wheel-chair?"

"Don't give up Honners —it's tennis this evening, between Benediction and Compline."

"Tennis! I've lost so much weight in this dump that I practically float away in a breeze as it is, and most of what's left is brain. Look at my suit—it hangs on me like a curtain. What are they trying to do, exterminate me? Give generously to the N.S.P.C.C. they keep telling you; stop all this cruelty to nippers, they moan; send every cent of your pocket-money to Save the Children Fund, they cry. I sent a whole shilling but nobody came down here to save me. At least they could have spared me a bowl of rice."

"The notice-board says it's your turn to serve at Mass tomorrow morning, Honners."

"Me again! Then all I can say is that it must be a Requiem Mass they're holding for me! I wouldn't put it past this mob to try and make you carry your own coffin."

"Don't keep talking, Honnerth," Elizabeth rebuked her partner. "You'll never learn to danth properly if you don't conthentrate on your stepth."

"Dry up and stop spitting over me like a scent-spray," Honners snapped irritably. "You should have more respect for your betters. Another lisp out of you and you're on my list of guests who are barred from Cudford Hall."

"My daddy'th a captain, tho there!"

"So was Captain Kidd, and look what happened to him—

they cut his bloomin' head off."

"Oh, you nathy, horrid little boy. . . ."

The quarrel was interrupted by Mother Phelan's call for all hands to muster for country dancing, or—as Honners called it—organized epilepsy. Daphne said to me, "Can you do country dancing, Peter?"

"I don't expect so—not unless it's anything like shadow-boxing."

"Well, hold my hand and, I'll show you. Oh, here's Raymond Zimmerman—I'd forgotten all about him."

Raymond ambled up with the gaucherie of youth, bowing to Daphne and sticking his tongue out at me. "It's my turn to dance with Daphne, Pook, so buzz off back to Australia with the other kangaroos," he declared.

"You're too fat to dance, Zimmerman. Go water the wallflowers again."

"Daphne's my partner for country dancing and if you don't buzz off I'll tell Mother Phelan."

"How will you be able to tell her with a fractured jaw?"

"Oh, please don't quarrel over me, boys—perhaps the three of us can dance together. I believe it's called a trio or something."

"I'm not dancing with Fatty!"

"I'm not dancing with Ugly!"

Up on the dais unsuspecting Mother Delaney was calling, "Now boys, listen carefully. When you hear the opening chord, turn to your partners and bow. Girls will curtsy. Everybody ready for the fun? Good—off we go!"

Hearing the chord, I turned to Daphne and bowed low as instructed, only to receive a violent blow on the back of my neck. Everything went blue, mixed with sparks, and I heard a voice saying, "Cheeky twit—that'll teach him to steal my partner. Tell him to curtsy next time—it's safer."

Suddenly the little girls ran screaming from the floor as I laid into Raymond with both hands. There was a violent scuffle

38

in the centre until Mother Delaney could descend from the dais and pull us apart. Raymond sat gasping on the floor, holding his stomach in pain, while Mother Delaney grasped my hair in one hand and Honners in the other, with unexpected strength for a nun. Blood was dripping from Honners' nose on to his dancing pumps, but for the life of me I couldn't figure how he was involved in the fracas except as an unfortunate bystander. Mother Phelan marched the pair of us off to Reverend Mother's study while Mother Delaney revived Raymond.

We had to stand before Reverend Mother's desk for the usual inquiry, but just as I was about to confess, Honners surprised me by saying he wanted to own up.

"I don't want the blame to fall on Ugly—er—I mean Peter, Reverend Mother, so I'll come clean. You know they're always sending me to Confession about my temper—well, Zimmerman barged into me during the dance and I was foolish enough to punch him. Afraid I rather overdid things and knocked the wind right out of him."

Honners rubbed his tiny fist to show where all the damage had come from.

"Do you mean to stand there, Honners, telling me you felled a boy twice your size and expecting me to believe you? Before you answer, let me remind you that you have also been sent to Confession for, shall we say, distorting the truth," Reverend Mother Blake declaimed coldly.

"Afraid so, Reverend Mother. My trouble is I don't know my own strength once I'm roused. I'll apologize to him, of course. At the moment I feel pretty ashamed of myself for being so brutal."

Reverend Mother Blake turned to me. "Did you strike Raymond?"

"Yes, ma'am, right in the solar plexus with my auctioneer."

"Why?"

"Because, being fat, that's his weakest spot."

"I mean why did you strike him at all."

"Oh, because he called me Ugly and told me to buzz off."

"So, Honners, after hearing Peter's testimony, do you still persist that you caused Raymond's distress?"

"Yes, ma'am, I do."

"Then why did you hit him so viciously in the stomach?"

"Because I'm too short to reach his jaw."

"And what was the outcome of your attack?"

"I got done on the snatch again, ma'am—that's why it's bleeding."

"So we deduce from the evidence that you both hit Raymond, but it was Peter's blow which incapacitated the unfortunate victim."

"Oh, no, ma'am," Honners stated confidently, "I was the one who floored the fat nit."

"Then I suggest, Honners, that if you are not actually telling an untruth you are boasting again. Next time you go to Confession for temper, tell God about bragging too. Now, both of you, kitchen fatigue for the remainder of the week, and never indulge in such ungentlemanly conduct while you are at this school—otherwise you may well find yourselves expelled. Dismiss."

"Isn't it marvellous, Peter," Honners said when we were safely outside the study, "my pater pays a small fortune to keep me at this high-class labour camp—so I can be a scullion stuck over the sink peeling spuds. Next time I meet the Duchess of Belter at one of her soirées I'll be able to bow low, parrot off the usual greeting clichés, then produce a bucket and scrubber for her ballroom floor."

"Forget it, Honners. What puzzles me is how you got mixed up in my argument. I didn't realize you had it in for Zimmerman."

Honners grinned smugly. "Anything's better than St.

Vitus's dance especially when you've got Elizabeth for a partner."

I left it at that.

Tennis began directly after Benediction, played as mixed foursomes amid the beautiful setting of trees in the Convent grounds. One of my most vivid recollections there is that of Honners marching onto the court in whites, holding a racquet almost as big as himself. In fact its size compelled him to use both hands, like a cricketer. He won't quarrel with me if I say that if he wasn't the world's best player he could certainly lay claim to being the world's worst loser.

He habitually rushed about the court, swiping the ball at all angles like a deranged butterfly collector, often missing and having a second hit—even altering the rules to suit his mistakes, such as insisting that under certain circumstances it was permissible for the ball to bounce twice before he got his racquet to it. His most maddening subterfuge, when he missed your shot completely, was to call "Out! Bad luck, Peter."

"What do you mean by out? It was well inside the line."

"Oh no, Peter, just outside, I'm afraid. See for yourself—there's the mark the ball made." Honners would then point to one of countless dents in the yellow playing-surface.

Another new rule Honners introduced permitted him to lean across the net to smash your shot, then fall over the net into your court on the follow-through. Provided his racquet did not touch the net in the process, this was a point to Honners. In addition, he introduced the revolutionary principle that if his two services hit the net he was allowed an extra ball to compensate for his lack of inches. Oddly enough, his opponents were bound by the conventional rules of the game.

This mode of play came to be known at the Convent as Honners' Rules, under which it was virtually impossible for him to lose a game. Even when he played our champion,

Raymond Zimmerman, Honners didn't lose. By some remarkable scoring on his part he produced an entirely new decision previously unknown in the world of tennis—a draw.

Yet it was to be Raymond Zimmerman who led to Honners' downfall on the courts. A big powerful lad for his age, Raymond was the only pupil at the school sufficiently skilled to have mastered the art of spin. His fast swerving service nearly sent Honners out of his mind, as he streaked about the court whirling the racquet at the balls in vain. He just could not judge the flight correctly, spinning round in the air with desperate attempts to hit balls which were never there, often falling about the court like a drunkard and filling the serene woodlands with oaths of frustration.

At first, Honners tried to introduce another new rule banning spin, but it is one thing to invent a rule and another to enforce it. Raymond Zimmerman delighted to torment Honners in this fashion, howling with glee as Honners swiped thin air and rolled in the dust as a consequence.

"You need a bigger bat, Honners," Raymond chided the little chap, who was picking himself up after a particularly wild miss. "Besides, you're supposed to play tennis standing up, not idling on your back in the sun. Forty love."

Honners struggled to control his voice. "You don't play fair, you overgrown ape! How am I supposed to hit the damn thing if you don't serve straight? Spin is all right for cricket, but this is meant to be tennis. Pack it up or I shan't play any more."

"You're windy, that's what you are. I'll pop over a slow one so you can see it. All you have to do is pat it back, then we can have a rally."

Raymond's slow one came down as fast as he could send it.

"Oo, lovely ace!" Daphne shrieked admiringly, as Honners' two-handed swipe missed the ball by a width.

"Lookth ath though Honnerth needth glathes," Elizabeth squealed.

"I don't need glasses, you female Flit-spray—I need silence to concentrate. Shove off before I ram a ball down your silly trap."

"Honnerth ith loothing hith temper again."

"I am *not* loothing, I mean losing my blasted temper, you nasty stupid little smell."

"You *are* loothing your temper just because you're loothing the game and thet. If you're not loothing your temper why do you keep thtamping your feet and thwearing at uth like a thavage?"

"Perhaps you'd be able to speak properly if you lost all your front teeth, you walking soda-siphon. . . ."

"Stop arguing and get on with the game," Raymond interrupted. "Advantage to me, remember?"

"Advantage to you? Not on your life. I thought it was deuce."

"How can it pothibly be deuth, Honnerth, when you've lotht every point so far, you thilly thing; you muthn't tell lieth on top of loothing your temper."

Honners flung his racquet down in disgust. "I positively refuse to play, with that lisping lunatic going off like a slow puncture. I'm begging you to shut up before I go off my nut. Take a walk outside, Elizabeth, and play with the traffic on the bypass."

"I'm not waiting any longer, Honners. I'm serving, and if you're not ready it's your own fault."

Honners crouched with slitted eyes in an agony of concentration in anticipation of Raymond's serve. Raymond wound up, then sent down his big one that hissed through the air. Honners leapt off the ground for his hammer stroke, only to miss the ball once more, as it ricocheted from the court to hit him in the face.

"Game, set and match!" Raymond roared triumphantly. "Now who's champion of England!"

In the best traditions of sport we had been taught to approach the net and shake hands, displaying that wonderful British trait of registering supreme bliss at being beaten, as though the object of the game was to lose. The two players ran to the net, but we stood aghast to see Honners congratulate Raymond by crowning him over the head with his racquet.

"That'll teach you to play fair, you rotten sport," Honners screamed, whacking Raymond to head and body, the better to impress upon him this valuable lesson in sportsmanship. Raymond began to blubber under the ferocity of the attack, desperately prodding his own racquet in Honners' red face to ward him off. Blood from Honners' nose began to leak down his shirt when Mother Phelan came running from the building as fast as her robes would permit, to separate the couple.

Such was the power of Honners' propaganda on the other children that little Audrey Featherstonhaugh was crying, "It's all Raymond's fault, Mother Phelan. He cheated and made poor Honners lose."

"How did he cheat, child?"

"He deliberately made the ball go crooked so poor Honners couldn't hit it. Everyone knows the rules say that's not fair. How can Honners win if Raymond cheats and won't let Honners bat the ball properly? Then he hit Honners, like the big horrid bully he is, and I shall never speak to him again as long as I live, so there."

Little Linda Temple was actually weeping because Honners had lost his unbeaten record. "Raymond should be punished for breaking the rules," she sobbed. "Honners told me himself that there's a special rule which says he isn't allowed to lose even if he wanted to."

Experienced teacher that she was, Mother Phelan quickly cut through the clutter of strange rules to the heart of the trouble, then marched Honners off to her study, leaving the other children to continue normal tennis without the game's energetic reformer.

By now, Honners was more concerned with his injury than the incident. "Whose nose wouldn't bleed to death if that great oaf clubbed it with a racquet. They'll have to give me a transfusion at this rate, unless they want to see me deflate like a balloon through loss of blood. Judging by the bread-and-skilly they serve in this workhouse for gentlefolk I don't think I could muster more than a pint anyway. Even my blasted legs are liable to snap like wishbones through lack of calcium. They're making me a martyr to haemophilia of the conk, so don't be surprised if I end up as a little red puddle with an identity disc floating in the middle of it."

"Silence, Honners, you wayward child! You must not allow your precocity to run away with you."

"I'm planning to run away on my own— Precocity can make her own arrangements. . . ."

"Stand in the corner and don't dare utter another word!"

After her lecture to Honners about sportsmanship and conduct becoming young gentlemen, Mother Phelan took a leaf out of his book by making up another rule concerning tennis— that Honners wasn't to play it for a whole month. Instead, we watched him march from the gardeners' shed with an axe over his shoulder in place of a racquet, in order to commence forest fatigue by thinning the silver birches that surrounded the Convent, on the grounds that his exhibition on the courts proved beyond doubt that he had mastered the art of tree-felling rather than tennis.

I shall always remember the look of melancholy in Honners' eyes as he trudged past me with the axe. "It speaks well of my opinion of you, Peter, that I prefer you personally should inform my next-of-kin. Don't make a fuss—we must all come to it in the end. Just tell them I went quietly and bravely, devoid of any bitterness, chopping away to the last till this dirty great axe slipped from these lifeless fingers and silence reigned once more in the forest. Think of me sometimes, when you sharpen a pencil or use a clothespeg, but try not to be miserable. Remember there comes a time when a little nobleman like me is better off out of his suffering on earth and gathered to the arms of his glorious forefathers in. . . ."

"Don't loiter, Honners," Mother Phelan called from her window, "there's plenty of work in those woods to keep you out of mischief until Compline."

Honners sighed. "Here I go, Peter—the Little Nell of the aristocracy. Farewell, old friend."

Faint chopping sounds, followed by a distant cry of "Timber!" floated across the air of that breathless summer eve, telling us that Honners had not yet departed this life, and our reassurance was completed when the rooks took flight in a body, disturbed by shrieks of "Fall, you blasted overgrown son of an acorn, or I'll tear you up by the roots!"

Mother Phelan discreetly closed her window.

THREE

Wanda Wells was so beautiful, with that transient perfection of sixteen, that when first we met I was struck dumb for the only time in my life. Wanda was a tall blonde possessed of a refulgent tan which made her teeth shine when she dimpled into a smile no camera could possibly capture. Worst of all, she was shy, which, what with my being struck dumb with calf love, led to electrified silences when we met each other on the beach. Then suddenly without warning she would break the spell with her husky voice, causing me to jump with a strange mixture of fright and excitement, so that the sweat flowed out of my pores and embarrassed me still further by bespattering the concrete ramp on which we sunbathed. Then it was essential for me to brace myself for the reply lest my voice issued in a shrill falsetto of nerves.

We passed our teens in the dream world of England just before the war, when life seemed enriched with a touch of elegance and the summers burned luxuriously for months on end; when people had time to practise the art of living and had not yet confused that subtle skill with the mere accumulation of material possessions which the modern exploitation agent tells us is Happiness.

Those awkward conversations between Wanda and me were remarkable only for their naievety. "What a lovely day for swimming, Peter."

After wiping the sweat from my forehead and body, and surreptitiously coughing to test my vocal chords for pitch, I would force myself to reply as one under tremendous tension. "Hm, hm. Yes indeed, Wanda, it certainly is a lovely day for swimming."

Then the long silence fell again, during which my left leg often developed a nervous tic, jerking so that I must hold it down forcibly, as though I had captured a live cod with my bare hands from the sea we both stared at with unnatural intensity. Wanda possessed a portable gramophone for music to fill in our long pauses between general observations on the weather and mutual friends. In fact the latter provided us with much of our dialogue, while in the background Bing Crosby sang to us non-stop about love in the mellifluous tones of sugar-land.

"That looks like Doreen over there, Peter."

"Hm, hm. So it is, Wanda. She is with Brian."

"I met her yesterday with Simon.'"

"I saw Helen with Martin the day before, Wanda."

"I wonder where Helen is today, Peter?"

"Helen and Doreen were here last week, Wanda."

"Yes, I know because Simon told me, Peter."

"Shall I ask Brian where Helen is, Wanda?

"Please don't bother, Peter. I'll ask Rosemary when I see her."

"I expect Richard will be along soon, Wanda. Perhaps he will bring Patricia."

"Oh, there's Norman coming down the beach now, Peter. I wonder if he has seen Sheila?"

One thing was certain, everybody saw Wanda and made straight for her—particularly Martin, Simon, Brian and the other bronzed giants of the sands. I dared not leave my perch next to Wanda for any pretext whatsoever, lest on my return I should be shut off from her by a wall of male flesh smelling of salt-water and that unsavoury concoction of coconut oil and vinegar we rubbed over our bodies to fry brown in such quantities that on a hot summer day our group atmosphere was redolent of a fish-and-chip stall. Above all, I dreaded the gramophone, which enabled Bing Crosby to join our party the livelong day. Winding it wasn't too bad, but the delicate business of changing the needle and replacing it on a fresh disc while Wanda stared at me with those soft green eyes brought on a nervous tic that scratched record after record. This was most upsetting for Bing, who began to repeat himself over and over again as though he could no longer exist on love alone but required food to stop his hiccups.

"I wouldn't like to see you thread a needle, Peter," Wanda remarked as I struggled to insert the pin like a drunkard trying his front door key.

I heard myself emitting a shrill ha-ha, which was supposed to be a deprecatory chuckle, and I wondered if it would be steadier to hold the needle between my lips. Once the task had been accomplished and the globules of sweat wiped off the record, I lay back to listen once more to Pennies from Heaven with that assumed pose of enthralment, as though we had not heard it continuously for three months.

One day Wanda and Doreen came walking up the beach after a swim, so immediately I switched on the little green box in which Bing lived, that he might greet the girls with a serenade of love and make up a foursome.

"Bing is in good voice today, Peter," Wanda called, shaking the flaxen tresses free of a bathing cap.

"He certainly is indeed, Wanda." I had long come to accept Bing as one of the group, but sometimes I wished he would go for a swim like the rest of us and husband his lungs a bit.

"Have you seen Simon yet, Peter?

"Hm, hm. No, Wanda, but Martin said he should be here soon."

"Perhaps he is with Helen."

"If I see Brian I will ask him, Wanda."

"Doreen saw him yesterday on the way to the beach."

"Goodness gracious, fancy that! I met Rosemary and she told me she had seen Simon. Simon told her he had just left Richard."

"Was Richard with Helen, Peter?"

"No, Wanda. I saw Helen later on her own, and she said

49

she was looking for Robert."

At the conclusion of the hide-and-seek saga, the girls discreetly dried themselves under huge towels like blankets, but Wanda discovered that the knot securing the halter of her swimsuit had shrunk so much in the water that she could not untie it. Doreen tried next, without success, despite vigorous work with a nail-file as a lever. I lay on a towel with my back to the girls in tactful pose, straining my eyes along the beach in search of Helen, Simon, Martin and Brian, and apparently spellbound by the lyric of Pennies from Heaven. Then Wanda called softly.

"I'm in an awful jam, Peter. I can't undo the knot of my halter, nor can Doreen."

"Hm, hm. Shall I see if I can find Helen, Wanda? She may be able to help? I said this because the girls of the day were surprisingly modest, and the division between the sexes was wider than we find in the permissive atmosphere of the contemporary scene.

"The knot is so tight that I'm sure she couldn't do any better than Doreen. Would you try for me, Peter?"

I stood closer to Wanda than ever before, marvelling at the perfection of her neck and shoulders. It seemed ridiculous that nature had bestowed so much beauty on one person when people like me were so short of it. She held her tresses out of the way with one hand, while the other primly clamped a towel round her waist. Sweat poured off me and my left leg began to jerk, but worst of all, my hands had suddenly sprouted ten thumbs, all incapable of grasping the wet knot. Instead, they slid clumsily over the fine golden hairs at the nape of her neck.

"Any joy, Peter?"

"Hm, hm. Afraid not, Wanda. The water has shrunk the knot into a tight ball."

"Oh dear! If you can't do it, I'm sure nobody can. My brother Paul told me how strong you are."

Which made it all the stranger that I should now be a shaky weakling, incapable of holding a knot. Embarrassed, I wiped my sweat off her back and resolved to show her how strong I was. I buried my teeth into the only accessible strand of the knot, braced my powerful, trapezium muscles, and heaved upwards.

I shall never forget Wanda's scream as the halter left her body in one piece. Momentarily she stood there motionless, her virgin breasts exposed to the light of day, and I remember thinking how white they were compared to the rest of her torso. Then she whipped up the towel to cover herself, while I stood there stupefied by events, with the halter still dangling from my teeth like a police dog who has ripped the pants off a criminal's backside.

Wanda and Doreen retired to dress in embarrassed silence, so I sought refuge in Bing Crosby's company and the eternal search of the beach for familiar faces.

Eventually Doreen came over to me, looking as though there had been a tragedy at sea. "Wanda is terribly upset about the incident just now, Peter."

"So am I, Doreen. I'm dreadfully sorry, but I had no idea. . . ."

"Of course not. She quite understands."

"Let me apologize to her now. . . ."

"No, Peter, that would only make her feel worse at the moment. It wasn't your fault really, but she says please not to mention it to any of the crowd. We're going now, so don't say anything."

"All I want to do is forget it, Doreen. Please apologize for me. . . ."

Only Bing was unruffled by the incident, singing his heart out all through the interview, just as he would do even if the city blew up behind us. As for myself, I was destined to do anything but forget the affair of the halter, chiefly because of

51

Wanda's brother, Paul. Strange how when you are determined to forget something you keep thinking about it, and Paul didn't help any. I could never figure out how a big tough character like Paul Wells could have been produced from the same stock which sired the breathtaking Wanda. Paul made no secret of the fact that not only was he the huskiest male in the district but also, despite his father's wish that he enter the Foreign Office, he was bent on becoming a professional wrestler.

Nearly black with sun and wind, Paul swam all year round —something I could never do—regularly appearing naked in the Christmas edition of the *Cudford Echo,* dominating a photograph captioned— 'Snowballing after his Yuletide dip.' or 'Breaking the ice doesn't mean that local tough guy is shy.' The summer editions of the *Echo* caught Paul whirling through the air over the heads of startled holidaymakers, to land with his bare shoulders on the shingle entitled—'One way to reach the sea when the beach is packed.' Another of his showpieces was to walk the length of the promenade upside-down on his hands, which the *Echo* described as 'Not an Australian visitor but iron-man Paul showing us the other side of his versatile personality.'

"They mean his backside," I commented at the time, secretly jealous of Paul's fame. Everybody laughed except Paul and, of course, Bing Crosby, who never allowed anything to interrupt his marathon romance in sugar-land. To compete with Paul in front of the girls, I made a habit of carrying the club boat down to the water on my head—a remarkable feat of sheer strength spoiled only by the fact that there was no earthly reason for doing it because there was a trolley provided.

Once, when Paul jeeringly pointed this out, I challenged him to lift the boat—and he failed. I knew he must fail because I had been practising this particular feat for two years, so, flushed with victory, I hoisted the boat on my head like a giant hat and walked along the crowded promenade, again for no apparent reason. Unbeknown to me, Tony Lynch, the *Echo* photographer, featured a half-page picture of my stunt in the evening edition, captioned 'I must go down to the seas again. . . .'

The whole town laughed except me, and the club committee fined me ten shillings for removing their boat from the premises.

The next clash with Paul occurred over the medicine-ball. All the local show-offs were competing on the beach to see who could throw the heavy bag furthest, using the life-guard hut as our target. Some of the lads could hurl it as far as the hut, but Paul could actually hit the hut wall. Seeing the girls watching, including Wanda, and already having learned the elements of showmanship, I threw the ball twice, each time just short of the hut but further than anyone except Paul.

"You're licked, Peter," he boasted. "Like I said, I'm the huskiest guy in Cudford—the only one who can hit the hut from the circle."

I smiled sportingly. "All right, Paul—you win. Tell you what though—we'll have another go, only this time we'll both throw with our left arms just to make it more difficult." I said this hoping he didn't know I was left-handed and had been throwing medicine-balls for eight years as part of my boxing schedule.

Paul laughed without humour. "You name your throw, Pook, and I'll top it. This is right up my street."

His first attempt was understandably clumsy, well short of the hut. My opening throw was even more awkward, carefully aimed to fall behind his. Everybody clapped.

"Tell you what we'll do, Paul, just to spice it up. The winner kisses your sister."

"What do I want with kissing my own sister?" he jested. "But you're on, just the same."

Paul poised the ball on his brown shoulder and heaved mightily, just hitting the base of the hut. The crowd roared approval and Paul called across to Wanda, "All right, sweetie, you're safe from Boatman."

I smiled modestly at Wanda, balancing the ball on my left shoulder and concentrating on those soft green eyes framed by the golden hair. Then I let the ball go to the sky.

Even I hadn't really thought it was possible to put the ball clean over the hut—but that's where it went, in a graceful arc. The spectators gasped for a second, then cheered delightedly.

"Sorry about that, Paul, it must have been a fluke," I told him unassumingly. "I was thinking about your sister at the time, figuring what a waste it would be if you won." So saying, I swaggered over to Wanda and pecked her chastely on the cheek, producing the deepest blush on a girl's face I had ever seen.

The jubilation of the crowd turned to dismay when an angry man came running round from the other side of the life-guard hut, demanding to know who had done it. He was followed by an equally angry woman, and this was the first time I had ever seen a person wearing a tent. The spectacle was so ludicrous that I burst out laughing, whereupon the lady wearing the red-and-white striped beach tent tried to extract her head from where it had perforated the roof of the tent.

"What happened?" I inquired.

"What happened?—it's a wonder my missus ain't killed. One of you louts threw a dirty great medicine-ball over that 'ut while my missus was undressing in our beach tent. Now look at the ruddy thing. Which one of you threw it, that's what I want to find out. . . ?"

Our set possessed many attractive talents, but undoubtedly the greatest of these lay in the field of magic, because only experts could disappear so mysteriously in full view of the public. The inexplicable melting away of so many large young men, however, was not to be the last of my feud with Paul.

The very next day it was clear that Paul had been finding out things from his cronies because he cornered me on the street with a hostile expression over his face, so that once again I marvelled that he could be related to such a perfect specimen of womanhood as Wanda. "You pulled a fast one on me yesterday and made me look sick in front of the mob, you lousy four-flusher," he snapped, in the cinema language of the day. "You deliberately stalled on the throws until you'd set up a winner for my sister by pretending you were right-handed."

"Blow, squirt—you give me ear-ache I told him, with a bored yawn. "Clump down the beach and practise with a ping-pong ball. Next time I'll let you stand half-way —you're strictly for the kiddies."

"Oh yeah!"

"Yeah!"

We stood like two young bulls of the herd disputing territory, and I wondered if I should have to break my promise to Constable Barrington about brawling in the street. Paul kindly settled the problem for me.

"No curly-haired gas-bag talks to me like that. You come back to my place and we'll settle it with gloves. Then you'll get a taste of this little mouth-shutter." Paul held up a singularly large mouth-shutter in the shape of his brown fist for my close inspection.

"You're kidding surely, Paul?" I suggested sympathetically. "Don't land me in any more trouble with the coppers—you're too young to die. Besides, it would upset your sister. Take a tip from a friend—you stick to the grunt-and-groan merchants and I'll stick to the classy punchers. That way you won't get hurt."

"If you don't come it's because you're yellow—all lip and no spunk. Take it or leave it."

The Wells's lived in a flat in a huge old Victorian building behind Cudford Crescent. I knew the place well by sight because I often walked past it in the hope of bumping into Wanda, so it held a certain fascination for me. Nevertheless, it never occurred to me that one day I should enter the place for the purpose of fighting her brother. Typical of these old buildings in town, there was nothing big enough to warrant the name of garden, so we had no option but to do battle in the flat itself. Paul told me that as his parents had gone to the cinema to see *All Quiet on the Western Front* we could settle our differences in the privacy of the kitchen where there was most room. It was certainly the biggest kitchen I had ever seen, but I advised Paul to place cushions over the gas-stove in case his head struck it as he went down. To increase the space to regulation size we carried the large wooden table into the scullery, then stripped to the waist and donned the battered eight-ounce gloves Paul pulled from a cupboard. In the dim light of the kitchen Paul's thick shoulders took on the hue of tanned leather, as we agreed to fight without rounds until one of us gave up.

"As there's no one here to throw the towel in, how will I know you're packing it in?" I asked him, loosening my own shoulders with air punches.

"You won't know, bud—you'll be asleep."

"Tell you what we'll do to make it fair, Paul. I'll shadowbox around and show you the fancy stuff while you try to lumber after me with those crude swings of yours. I won't clout you, apart from light left leads to let you know where I am."

"All right, Pook, I'll tell you a little secret. I deliberately got you to fight in my kitchen so you can't tango out of trouble, like you would in a full-size ring. Here I can really nail you to the wall like a batten. Let's go."

As Captain and Mrs Wells sat in the Troxy watching *All Quiet on the Western Front,* they little suspected the carnage taking place on the home front. I tapped Paul's nose playfully with the left as a sop to his pride, at the same time observing his flailing fists circle about the kitchen like asteroids in orbit. I regarded him quizzically—surely you weren't expected to teach a man to box before you could have a grudge fight with him? Nevertheless, I gave him as much advice as was permissible under the circumstances—chiefly because of his relationship to Wanda—not a simple task when your opponent is grunting and snuffling like a hedgehog.

Dancing with easy grace on my toes, I skilfully slipped his right as he rushed me against the kitchen cabinet. This tremendous right went clean through the glass door of the cabinet, to disintegrate the dishes inside. The noise of falling glassware was so appalling that I dropped my guard, whereupon Paul repeated the punch, thus ramming my head into the teacup section of the same cabinet.

"Nailed you at last, Slackarse the Fearless," he roared triumphantly, hooking lefts and rights into me.

It was then I realized that, big as he was, he couldn't punch —merely destroying his mother's crockery with my head. So, pausing only to wipe blood off my face with a tea-towel and step out of the kitchen cabinet, I began to set him up for the finale.

"All right, Paul, so you want to play it rough, eh? Just show me where's best for you to fall and I'll out you."

After softening him up with some crisp body rockets to take his mind off his jaw, I orientated him clear of the gas-stove, then fired the left hook. It streaked home on target but even I hadn't expected to see Paul go through the wall as a result. I recall a crackling sound of plywood and nails squeaking out of battens, and flakes of distemper floating down from the ceiling—but most horrible of all was the scream.

Paul's feet were still protruding into the kitchen, but from his invisible end I heard a splashing noise accompanied by shrieks of fear. Bewildered, I leaned over Paul's knees into another room. This action on my part produced the second horrific scream. Immediately below my chest was Wanda sitting in a bath, with her brother's shoulders resting on her shins. All she had on was a plastic hair-snood protecting the golden locks.

Apparently the bath water had revived Paul, because he was shouting for me to pull him out. Simultaneously, Wanda was screaming for me to go away, so, modestly averting my eyes, I hauled at Paul's feet with all my might in order to pull him back into the kitchen. I succeeded, but the effort combined with Paul's weight tore the partition from the remaining battens in the process. Now, a twenty-foot section of plywood and wallpaper lay across the kitchen floor, completely exposing the bath in which Wanda was crouched, betrayed only by the top of the hair-snood.

Wanda continued to shout for us to leave the kitchen but I couldn't extricate Paul from the hole in the dividing partition. Its collapse had wedged him firmly in the aperture he went through originally. Even worse, I couldn't get my boxing-gloves off because there was no way for me to untie the knots of the laces.

"Paul's trapped in the dividing partition, Wanda," I tried to explain, lest she thought I was a Peeping Tom.

"Get out! Get out of the flat, you hooligan you! Don't ever let me see you again," she cried desperately.

"Take the weight of the partition off me and perhaps I can crawl out." It was Paul's voice from under the debris, so, dismissing a thought of asking Wanda to assist me, I knelt down to get my shoulder under the top of the partition and heaved. With much rending of plywood Paul managed to slide his body free of the hole—just as Captain and Mrs Wells entered the flat.

The couple peered through the dust at the scene in amazement, trying to take in the wreckage which had once been home.

"Peter and I have been boxing," Paul explained wretchedly.

Captain Wells was the first to recover his wits. "Boxing! Boxing! Boxing!" he repeated, baffled by the connexion between boxing and the destruction of his premises. "Where's Wanda? Is she safe?"

"She's over there in the bath, father."

"Why in hell's name is she taking a bath at a time like this? Have you all taken leave of your senses?"

Mrs Wells uttered a maternal cry and climbed over the debris to her daughter, then shouted for us to leave the room while Wanda was helped out of the bath. During this interval I glanced at Captain Wells's red face and feared for his reason. It was beyond my comprehension how anybody could possibly explain the events of the afternoon. I certainly didn't feel equal to such a task, so I quietly backed down the stairs, in the belief that family matters are best avoided by outsiders, and glided unnoticed through the front door.

Cornstable Barrington of the all-seeing eye picked me up half-way along Cudford Crescent, with the request that I accompany him to the police station for interview just because I happened to be wearing boxing-gloves and shorts in public.

"Then if it's true you often walks about the town wearing eight-ounce gloves to keep your mitts warm, how come your naked body ain't froze?" he demanded, in answer to my explanation. "You quite sure you're telling me the truth for once, Pook? Perhaps it's to stop you biting your nails, eh?"

"I am not in the habit of biting my nails Constable Barrington, despite the way you haunt my every waking moment."

"Then how come you scratched yourself? There's the remains of blood all over your clock and shoulders. And don't tell me you washes yourself with Bovril instead of soap."

"Look, constable, you know very well I do a bit of boxing for the county, so why shouldn't I nip home from the gym in my kit because I'm late for tea?"

"Ho, ho, so you been fighting again, eh Pook? If you're so handy with your dukes how come you cut the back of your head? You learned to box backwards as well?

"Unfortunately during the sparring session my head accidentally broke a saucer. Now I'll be on my way if you don't mind."

"If you was sparring in the gym, like you says, how come there was a saucer behind you? What were you wearing on your head at the time—a teacup?"

Over the years I had to give Constable Barrington many outlandish explanations for my conduct, such as creeping home from a New Year's Eve party through an upper window, only to find myself in Mrs Sopworth's bedroom next door instead of my own, then trying to convince Barrington that I suspected there was a burglar prowling the area. "Yes, Pook," he had sneered," and it looks like I've caught him redhanded—unless you've got desperate and fancies Mrs S."

"Do me a favour, constable, and stop bothering me with puerile questions when I'm in training. It's too late for promotion at your time of life, so just waddle off down the road and fill up your bull's-eye lantern ready for tonight, in case you find me creating a breach of the peace by kissing my girl in our porch after curfew—I know you never go off duty."

"Better still, Pook, I'll take the precaution of jotting down this little incident in me book, then when the complaint comes in from wherever you been this afternoon we can put two and two together and charge you. The Superintendent's already had a holidaymaker down the station, raving about some big nut knocking his wife through her beach-tent with an offensive weapon—a medicine-ball, I think he said. Not that it concerns you because I expects you was over in North Africa all yesterday, fixing up your alibi with Ali Baba. Now push off home, and don't forget to brush the plaster out of your hair afore you puts your snogging suit on for tonight's orgy."

"Good night sweet prince, and flights of angels sing thee to thy rest!"

FOUR

Honners appointed himself my manager directly the news of my battle with Paul Wells grass-fired round Cudford as fast as Honners' little legs could carry it. He was furious on two counts. First, he had not been present at the contest, and second, that I had sunk to fighting secretly in somebody's kitchen.

"If I don't handle you, you'll end up brawling in public conveniences," he reprimanded me sternly. "If everybody acted like you, we'd be playing the Test matches against Australia on the Corporation muck tip by now. Where's your professional pride, that's what I want to know? In future I'll arrange your fights, train you, and try to keep you out of the gutter."

One thing about having Honners as your manager, you were never short of opponents. Much of this advantage was due to the ancient battle-cry of the Pilkington-Goldbergs, or, more accurately, Honners' interpretation of it. The original battle-cry of the family had first been used at Crécy in 1346, when Sir Walter de Pilkington had taunted the French by shouting in Latin 'Come forth, ye reluctant knights, and do battle with your betters.' We know the French knights understood Latin because they came forth immediately, and that is the last we hear of Sir Walter until 1350, when the family had saved sufficient money to pay his ransom. As Honners never tired of telling me, it was a waste of time shouting Latin at the modern yob, so there was no alternative but to translate the cry into English, which he construed as 'Come out and fight you son-of-a-bitch.' Readers may recall how on more than one occasion the injudicious use of the battle-cry brought people out to fight who previously had not been involved. The classic example of this occurred in 1862, during the American Civil War, when Percy Pilkington-Goldberg—still remembered affectionately as Gunpowder Percy, the Mounted Maniac—rode up and down the town by night, shouting 'Come out and fight, you son-of-a-bitch', until the citizens responded to such good effect that the town centre was razed to the ground by dawn. As a result, Percy Pilkington-Goldberg was tried at Cudford Assizes for attempting to introduce the American Civil War into England overnight, found guilty but insane, and only saved from the gallows by the 8th Earl's offer to rebuild the centre of Cudford as we know it today. In the market square you may still see the statue erected to his memory by the Aldermen, whereon the inscription refers to him as the instigator of the celebrated Cudford Riots of 1862, and, paradoxically enough, the founder of the new town centre.

The first contest under my new management was against one Ivor Evans, apprentice fitter at Cudford Motors Ltd., High Street. It happened this way. In the summer the Headmaster of Cudford Grammar School, Dr Windebank, insisted that all senior boys wore straw boaters decorated with their house colours. My route to and from school took me through the High Street and past Cudford Motors Ltd., where the apprentices' favourite sport was to await my arrival, often with Honners, then air their wit on our unusual headgear—known in the repair trade as a brake-drum, although some of the apprentices insisted that it was a clutch-plate.

"Why do you wear that brake-drum on your nut, cocky?" they chanted every day at 4.30. "Is it to stop your head going round and round?"

"That ain't no brake-drum, mate. He can't afford a proper 'at, so he wears a clutch-plate. Watch him change gear at the corner with his big ears. Left foot down hard, cocky, then put your ears in neutral and double-declutch. Rev up with the right foot, let your nose out gently so your clutch-plate don't wear out and fall off. . . ."

"Go play with your nuts and bolts, Greasy-face," I shouted back angrily. Extremely difficult to walk along the High Street with dignity when the locals are laughing at your discomfiture.

"It ain't a clutch-plate, mate, because it talks," Apprentice

Wally Dane roared delightedly. "Must be a potty for his little friend Honners. Hey, Short-arse the Bold, why do you let your footman carry your wee potty upside-down?"

"No, mate, it can't belong to Short-arse the Bold because he's wearing his very own potty up on his conker, with a special pretty ribbon round it, all coloured to show it's his very own Bo-Peep potty and no-one else's. Fancy having the nerve to go for wallkies down the High Street and show everybody their little potties. . . ."

"Don't call out to your betters, lads. Remember your humble station in life for failures, then crawl back into your grease-pits like good little guttersnipes."

The apprentices never tired of baiting us about the strawboaters, but Honners refused to be drawn. Red faced, eyes and nose dilated, he marched determinedly by, lest he have a fit in public. I didn't really mind the chaff each day but one apprentice in particular got under my skin. I happened to bump into Wanda near the garage one afternoon, and just as she began to ask me if I had seen Mark and, if so, was he with Helen, a head appeared from the window above and the dreaded Welsh accent started. "Well, well, I ain't never seen a bloke carrying his spare wheel on his head before. Must have had a puncture, look you. Excuse me, kind sir, I know you've had a puncture like, but shouldn't you raise your spare wheel when you meets a lady, bach? Perhaps it would help if I lent you a jack, then we could lift your legs up and fit the spare wheel underneath your. . . ."

Ivor Evans could do his worst but I had no intention of making a scene before Wanda, of all people, so I ignored it. Even at this stage nothing would have come of the childish business if Honners had not become involved. Of course, he offered a sitting target for the apprentices and they made the most of it, although in fairness to Honners it must be said that he steadfastly refused to be drawn into what he was pleased to call the entertainments of the sewer people. But the apprentices had another card up their sleeve, which was to lean down from the windows as we passed and flick our boaters off with sticks. This manoeuvre was particularly effective on windy days, when we had to chase after the hats as they bowled down the High Street.

"Hallo, Dustbin," Wally Dane shouted to Honners. "What's the point of being a dustbin if you don't take your lid off so we can ditch our gash in yer?" With that, Ivor Evans neatly flipped Honners' hat off from behind with a long stick.

Honners was furious, as only Honners could be. "Come down here, you oily-faced smell, and I'll teach you to knock my titfer off!"

"He's too little to be a dustbin—he's more of a Harpic bottle! Watcher, Harpic—are you round the bend?"

Seldom had I seen my friend so enraged before. Stamping his feet and brandishing his tiny fists at the window, he played right into the apprentices' hands by screaming "Come out here, you leek-eating savage, and I'll wipe that smirk off your windscreen!"

All the apprentices laughed delightedly at having got Honners at last. Ivor shouted "No, you come in here, Harpic, so we can flush you down the toilets," then all the faces at the windows took up the chorus of 'Harpic is a dwarf's best friend'.

Obviously the stupid business of name-slinging had gone too far and I tried to lead Honners away, but he stood there trembling with rage. At first he couldn't speak but when he regained control of his voice he suddenly began to shriek the fatal battle-cry over and over again, like one demented. Still yelling "Come out and fight, you son-of-a-bitch", he strode into the workshops, roaring abuse at the apprentices and waving a car jack about as if it were a mace of old.

"Crawl out and fight a titled toff, you grease-monkey— I'll Harpic every one of you!" he threatened, without specifying how he intended to thrash such large young men with big nut-tightening arms, but Honners' ferocious little figure only made the apprentices laugh the more. Although we didn't suspect it at the time, Mr Clements, the service manager, was even then on the phone reporting Honners to our Headmaster because of the language he was roaring through the workshops—language not usually associated with the aristocracy.

As Honners passed a van his straw boater was again mysteriously knocked off his head, whereupon my friend went almost berserk, running round the benches and waving the car jack in an effort to get to grips with his tormenters. The apprentices easily dodged his rushes, playing a kind of hide-and-seek among the vehicles with delighted enthusiasm at this break in routine. The chase was halted by Mr Clements who emerged from his office and ordered Honners to leave the premises forthwith. Much out of breath, Honners strutted off with as much dignity as he could muster, till Ivor Evans called out, "Don't forget your dustbin lid, Short-arse the Bold."

Honners bent down and picked up his soiled boater, slapped it impatiently on his head, then turned slowly round as he realized that a large dollop of bearing grease was now securing the hat to his hair. This really was the last straw, and momentarily I thought Honners was about to have a stroke at the early age of sixteen. With a demoniac scream to the effect that he intended disembowelling the Welsh car-wrecker with his bare hands though he swing for it, Honners flew at Ivor like a rabid terrier, raining blows as fast as his little arms could circle—none of which landed because Ivor goodnaturedly held him at arms' length by means of a hand as big as the face it covered. Several of the cheering spectators tried to knock Honners' boater off but for once it was stuck fast.

On Mr Clements' orders the apprentices picked Honners up and carried him bodily from the workshops, still punching, kicking and calling on the gods to let him be revenged on all

Welshmen, but Ivor Evans in particular. Once outside, Honners found the door barred against him, but still he continued to kick and bang it, at the same time informing the local populace that if necessary he would tear down Cudford Motors Ltd. brick by brick, in order to dismember his tormentor.

"Hallo, hallo, what have we here then?" Constable Barrington inquired in that maddeningly slow speech adopted by the Law when addressing lunatics. "Worked ourselves up into a right old paddy again, eh? Attempting to damage private property and uttering threats against another party, eh?"

Honners stopped in full blast for a moment to see who the intruder was. "Oh my God, Eternity sent down to earth in human form! Don't just stand there gibbering to yourself, Barrington, unless you want me to go off my onion. Try and do something constructive for once before you retire, by arresting that vandal in there who has sabotaged my boater with a dirty great dollop of car grease. Look at the mess I'm in. . . ."

"Right again, Honners—you're in a mess with the Law, going on like. . . ."

"Save it for your memoirs, Barrington, and concentrate on the evidence." Honners raised his hat as far as his hair would allow. "Look at the muck—ruined the titfer and congealed my hair. Arrest the big ape and don't let him plead insanity—he may be a nut but at least they permit him to work in a public place."

"My, my, we are in a right old tiz, aren't we, Honners?" Constable Barrington pulled out the notebook we knew so well. Honners glared at it with bared teeth.

"All right, constable, we're aware you've mastered the art of writing pidgin English, but this is a time for action—you know, when you have to do something without composing an essay about it first. Look, you can write it up in the months ahead. If a reporter sees Cudford Castle on fire he doesn't go home and type a story about how William the Conqueror built it in 1070—he rushes to the scene and tries to get in. We know your motto is Time Heals All, but this is a case where you'll have to break it for once by actually doing something urgent before pension."

"Ho, ho, so our tiny titled toff is coming the acid again, eh? Trying to change procedure, eh? Time we learned that we can't do nothing without all the relevant facts down in black and white. Once on paper we knows where we are—then we can charge you, you saucy little thug."

"Charge me!" Honners' voice shrilled up in indignation.

"Damaging private property; creating a breach of the peace; using obscene language on the King's highway; causing an obstruction on a public footpath; threatening an officer of the law in the course of his duties. These are the obvious charges, then we come to the less familiar ones, such as. . . ."

Knowing Constable Barrington so well, I hurried Honners away before we became involved in the impossible task of defeating him at his own game.

Dr Windebank had no option but to cane Honners for his behaviour in the car workshops, but caning Honners was about as effective as beating a carpet. Honners didn't mind the punishment. "We Pilkington-Goldbergs have always been brought up to regard pain as a form of pleasure. Flog me, I say, that my soul may overflow with rapture"—but he brooded bitterly over the grease episode. "If the Industrial Revolution breeds trained monkeys who are allowed to assault a blue-blooded nob without let or hindrance and call him gutter names, then Britain may as well go the whole hog and join the Commees," he declared. "Anyhow, the next time I see that obnoxious Taff I'll thrash him within an inch of his wretched life."

Apart from the threats, Honners never specified how he intended thrashing a brawny apprentice twice his size. I pointed out this detail but he waived the objection aside. "Breeding,

Peter, that's the secret. Breeding will always vanquish brawn, that's why you don't hear of a cart-horse winning the Derby. Take your case, for instance; all muscle and no brain—like a curly-headed dinosaur. That's why I'm your manager."

"But they bred you too small, Honners—probably forgot to put the yeast in to make you rise. You'll get murdered."

"As I say, Peter, your brain is like your appendix —present but useless. No doubt, generations ago, the Pooks were able to think with it like normal psychopaths, but over the years it's become atrophied until today it's merely a space-filler to prevent your scalp caving in."

"But what about the Head's warning and expelling you if there's any more trouble at Cudford Motors? Is it worth it?"

Honners sniffed. "He wouldn't dare expel me, Peter—I'm the only Debrett macaroni on the books. Much more lip from Windebank and I'll transfer to Harrow, where I should have been in the first place if my old man hadn't gone off his rocker about democracy and seeing how the other half lives, so you can rule it better later on. As far as I'm concerned you can keep your half—it makes my nose bleed."

Nevertheless, despite the big talk, Honners was finally convinced it would be foolish to incur the wrath of Dr Windebank any further, so we agreed that Honners' injured pride would be satisfied if I fought Ivor Evans instead. Honners refused to negotiate direct with Ivor, demanding that Wally Dane should act as Ivor's second, as though we were arranging a duel.

The apprentices finished work at five, so the contest took place at 5.15 the following Friday in the huge loft above the workshops, with all the staff of Cudford Motors as spectators. Mr Clements agreed to act as referee. Ivor was a big strong lad of eighteen who knew as much about boxing as I knew about boring a cylinder. Cheered on by his mates, Ivor rushed me and swung his thick arms in vain, while I prodded him off and danced round the boards waiting to sell him the big punch.

"You should have taken my advice and used the big sixteen-ounce gloves, Ivor," I told him during a clinch, "then you wouldn't have got cut up so much."

Ivor snorted. "Don't give me excuses, Pook—you've got it coming to you the hard way. Time someone took you down a peg or two." With that, he was foolish enough to drop his guard and bombard me at close quarters, which I thwarted by neatly falling over the ropes into the spectators. This was really playing into my hands because it lulled Ivor into a sense of false security, enabling me to indulge in a few more tricks I always set up to entertain the audience and confuse the opposition. The most spectacular of these is the fast-moving Tango Turn, whereby one changes direction so quickly and unexpectedly that one's opponent is left facing thin air, wondering if you have gone through the floor. I tried this out on Ivor, because it allowed me to do two things; first, without warning I was standing right behind him, positioned for the kill the moment he turned round, and the second didn't matter because Ivor's lack of experience in the ring made him bungle a beautiful manoeuvre by throwing such a barrage of blows in a desperate attempt to ward off my auctioneer that once again I skilfully evaded trouble by leaving the ring upside-down.

Although basically of ice-cold temperament, I chuckled sportingly at the success of my tactics as Honners helped me back over the ropes. "Stop clowning, Peter, and bash his potty off once and for all," Honners advised me sharply. "If he knocks you out of the ring three times in a row he'll get the idea that he's winning or something."

"No need to worry, pal—just giving the lads their money's worth by encouraging Ivor to put up some kind of show. My trouble is I hit so hard I should be banned from amateur boxing."

Ivor was so elated at his apparent success that he had the nerve to crow. "Nailed you good and proper that time, didn't I, bach? No point in boxing clever, man, if you have to do it outside the ring, look you."

"If you possessed any knowledge at all of the game you'd have seen how I rode the punch all the way, just to kid you along and spice things up a bit—look you, bach."

"Next time try riding a horse—you won't go so far, man."

The Welsh accent was bad enough but I drew the line at Ivor's jokes. Surely he didn't intend flooding the place with *Land of Our Fathers* between rounds.

During the second round, my appraisal of the opposition completed, I battered Ivor so soundly about the body that it was a miracle how he found the strength to retaliate. I knelt down for a short count, partly to think things over and partly for dramatic effect, rose to my feet at eight, only to be as startled as Ivor by a piercing scream of "Come out and fight, you son-of-a-bitch!" from my own corner. Ivor turned round to see the source of such venom, whereupon I couldn't resist the temptation to explode the left hook to his stomach. Ivor folded up like an ironing-board, clamping the damaged area and swearing violently in English, while Mr Clements gave him the slowest count I had ever heard. Ivor was still kneeling and swearing at nine, when Mr Clements, who was also timekeeper, said "Time! End of round two."

"Since when have rounds been of two-and-a-half minutes duration?" Honners shouted angrily. "He's out and you know it."

'Sorry, but the bell saved him, Honners."

"Of course the bell saved him. If you count seven, eight, nine, Time, whenever he's in trouble how can he possibly lose? I suppose the next round will drag out to nearly a minute-and-three-quarters."

"Are you accusing me of favouring one of the contestants by shortening the rounds?

"Oh no! You just forgot how to tell the time, that's all."

"Why, you nasty-minded little squirt!"

"How dare you, sir! No jumped-up banger-merchant in a white coat is going to call me nasty-minded."

"All right then, so you're a clean-minded little squirt. Now close your air-intake jet and shut up, then we might be able to get on with the fight."

It was always a mystery to me why Honners chose such big fellows to row with, because round three suddenly commenced with a flurry of blows between Honners and Mr Clements, as though the rules permitted substitutes as in football. Honners was punctuating his attack by informing the startled spectators that they were about to witness the fate of unscrupulous petrol-pump attendants who were rude to a top-crust macaroni of the blood—rash predictions under the circumstances because his tiny fists were having no effect whatsoever on Mr Clements. On the other hand, Honners' retroussé nose was now flat and red, like a crushed strawberry, leaking some of the noble blood for general inspection.

Honners sat on the floor, holding a handkerchief to the seat of the damage. "Damn and blast it, my snuff-box always spurts every time I wallop somebody," he gasped weakly. "Just when I had that mouthy windscreen-wiper at my mercy some cow bashed my beak with a hammer."

"It was this what done it, you vicious little twit," Mr Clements informed him, showing a large tattooed fist marked *Love Thy Neighbour - and Molly,"* and you'll taste it again if you accuse me of dishonesty in a scrap. Now clear off so we can re-start the main bout."

"Which is between you and me," I told him angrily. "Ivor has had enough, but I didn't like the way you flattened Honners —he's not half your size. . . ."

"Don't interfere, Peter," Honners insisted savagely. "I can handle this bum as soon as my nostrils come to the surface for air. Put the gloves on me, someone, then stand back to catch

71

his corpse."

Mr Clements laughed ironically. "Look, matey, if you really are tired of life there's little Alfie over here. He's the smallest apprentice on the books, and certainly more your size. You can have a go with him, if you like, then we'll inform your next-of-kin through the usual channels."

Honners glared distastefully at Alfie. "Me fight that freckle-faced midget? Don't be so unkind. I don't want to find myself in court on a manslaughter charge."

Being taller than Honners, Alfie took the strongest objection to the appellation of freckle-faced midget, and said so. Despite the general confusion, everybody approved the match, so both youths were speedily gloved and, without waiting for such formalities as bells, flew at each other like two windmills in a gale. There was no pretence of science, just non-stop attack, as though the object was to hammer one's opponent into the boards like a nail.

The fury of the contest ensured that it couldn't possibly last more than a few minutes, and provided the first occasion we had ever seen a boxer go down on his knees still punching. Honners took so much leather in his face that he had no option but to fight on even after his little legs collapsed under him. While Mr Clements dragged Alfie off him, I tried to staunch the blood from Honners' nose, but his mouth was cut at both ends and the left eye completely closed.

As I dabbed the injured parts Honners was gasping, "I've got the measure of the sawn-off runt all right, Peter. That was only the warm-up—next round he goes clean out of the ring on his ear."

"There isn't going to be a next round, pal. They've had to stop the fight," I told him sadly.

"So he quit, eh? Typical of the working-class. Just as I was about to thrash him in front of his own morons."

"Have it your own way, chum, but the general impression

is that he's too big for you and you've had enough."

Honners' cut mouth dropped open with incredulity. "Had enough! Don't let Clements get away with it, Peter. I was merely letting him burn himself out before I stiffened him for keeps. Come out and fight, you son-of-a-bitch!"

Sadly I lifted Honners to his feet while somebody pulled the gloves off. I wondered even then what Dr Windebank would say on Monday when he saw the state of Honners' face.

As we left Cudford Motors Ltd., several of the apprentices slapped Honners on the back, accompanied by friendly remarks about his pluck, and Mr Clements muttered something about wishing he hadn't reported anything to Dr Windebank.

Although Honners was well and truly beaten in the ring that evening it was noticeable that never again did anyone tip his straw boater off as he strutted aggressively down the High Street, even though he occasionally peered in through the workshop windows to roar the ancient Pilkington-Goldberg battle-cry of "Come out and fight, you son-of-a-bitch!"

FIVE

One of the snags about wooing Wanda Wells was the question of food. Thinking about her made me so excited that I couldn't eat, with the result that when she had been in my company for an hour I was too weak to do anything about it. Worse still was the dreaded return of appetite after two hours, when even the beautiful Wanda temporarily lost some of her charm for me as I drooled for food like a starving mountaineer trapped on the Matterhorn.

I remember vividly my first hard-won date with Wanda. Smarmy Mark Liddell, handsome rugby maniac, had gone to South Africa in order to play all the year round a game most people reckon is bad enough in winter, leaving the field open for me. When the remaining male competition had rushed into the sea for the first dip of the day I craftily halted at the water's edge and rushed back up again to where Wanda was in conference with Bing Crosby. Ignoring Bing, I asked her if she would go alone with me to Lark Island by boat, and was thrilled to hear her agree. I stressed about going alone because the last thing I wanted was to spend the day on Lark Island with Wanda and Cudford Rugby fifteen in trunks, turning the beach into a kind of Twickenham by the sea. During the week of waiting for the hard-won date I was so excited and lovesick with anticipation that meals became virtually repellent to me, to the extent that my parents feared I must be sickening for gastro-enteritis.

By good fortune the great day dawned as fine a morning as summer can produce; hot, windless, and the sea so still that one felt tempted to walk on the glassy surface. I rose at six to complete my toilet with elaborate care because I was to call for Wanda at nine. All went well, except for shaving. In order to polish my chin beyond reproach I used a new blade for the first time, giving my parents the impression that I had tried to commit suicide in the bathroom. Nevertheless, I swamped the area with Napoleon's Secret after-shave lotion, then applied five tiny plasters to the damage to stem the blood flow. Next, I dressed carefully in the smart boating attire of the day—white shirt and blazer, floral cravat, white trousers with black-and-cream shoes. To complete the picture I daringly cocked a straw boater on my head, then skilfully arranged a curl on the free side.

The prospect of the delights ahead so excited me that I partook of only one cup of tea, and even this was in danger of being regurgitated. Although Wanda lived only ten minutes away I left home at eight and waited round the corner for nine o'clock. During this long interval Wally Dane cycled past, calling out "Watcher, poof! Didn't know you'd joined the Kentucky Minstrels. Where's yer banjo then?" but I ignored it. Directly the town clock struck nine I marched round the corner, and knocked boldly at the door of the flat.

Wearing dressing-gown and curlers, Mrs Wells opened the door and started back in surprise. "Good morning, Peter—it is Peter, isn't it? I thought you were taking Wanda to Lark Island. She didn't mention anything about a party."

"That's correct, Mrs Wells, but there isn't any party."

"Then why are you all dressed up like that?

"Oh, this." My mind raced around trying to think of an explanation. I blurted out the only available inspiration. "It's my birthday, Mrs Wells."

"Then many happy returns of the day, Peter. I'll just see if Wanda is up."

"Up!" I prayed Wanda might be not only up but ready, because the last thing I wanted was for her brother Paul to see me in the garb of an Edwardian punt poler.

Wanda was so long putting in an appearance that I began to wonder if she was even at home, unless she was lying in bed drugged. This latter suspicion was confirmed when Mrs Wells reappeared as the town clock struck 9.30, to announce that she had managed to wake her daughter and get her out of bed. "Perhaps you would like to come in, Peter, while she has her breakfast. She's so tired after the Rugby Club's summer ball last night. Marcus didn't bring her home till nearly three."

I waited in the front parlour with the feeling that I was destined to spend my day out in Mrs Wells's flat while her daughter dozed the hours away upstairs. My fears were not allayed by regular calls from the kitchen of "Wanda, are you up yet?" Perhaps she was having breakfast in bed. "Graham, if you're awake pop in and see what's happened to Wanda. Peter's waiting downstairs for her. Paul, hurry up—breakfast is cooking. Graham, please go to Paul's room and wake him up. Graham, Graham, don't tell me you're still asleep! Wanda, see what's happened to your father—he doesn't answer and the bacon is frizzling up. Wanda! Oh, what's the matter with the child? I told you hours ago Peter is here. Paul! Can you knock on your sister's wall, please? Graham, the least you can do for me is to get the children up. Graham, can't you answer me for once?"

I listened mournfully to the house of the dead. Not a soul replied from upstairs and I began to wonder if Mrs Wells had shot her entire family during the night. A deep snore penetrated the ceiling of the parlour to reassure me, as Mrs Wells entered the room again. "Terribly sorry to keep you waiting so long, Peter, but we had such a disturbed night, what with Wanda coming in at three and Paul knocking us up even later. My husband often has to rouse Paul by dragging him out of bed but Wanda is usually up with the lark. She must have dropped off again, so I'll pop up myself. Here's Punch, if you would like to read."

I scanned the jokes in Punch with a very long face indeed, thinking to myself things must be pretty bad if even Bing is silent, snoring away in his little box in Wanda's bedroom. An unromantic urge gripped me to tiptoe upstairs with a bucket of cold water, but this was stifled by a heavy thud from the floor above, caused presumably by Paul's senseless body being dragged out of bed by his mother.

Wanda finally made it around ten-five, and when she came through the door, a blaze of technicolor gold, green and red, I gaped at her as always, dropping *Punch* and temporarily losing the power of speech.

"Good gracious, Peter, I thought you were in fancy dress— you might have come straight from the Rugby Club's summer ball last night!" she purred, tossing back the long golden tresses. "But what a glorious rose in your buttonhole."

I swallowed, trying surreptitiously to recover my wits, then began testing my voice for pitch by coughing affectedly. I was shocked to hear my reply emerge in the tight falsetto of nervous tension. "Ha, ha! Fancy dress, eh? Ha, ha! The rose is for you, Wanda. Ha, ha!"

The added lie about the rose sent my false laugh up to an almost hysterical shriek and my left leg began to jerk uncontrollably so that I was forced to hold it down. Until meeting Wanda I had not known the meaning of nerves but nowadays my condition was so pronounced that I suffered a layman's fear of epilepsy.

"Have you a car today, Peter?"

"Ha, ha! A car, eh? Of course, Wanda; only the best is good enough for you. Cudford Corporation are sending it round at 10.31. Ha, ha!"

This was meant as a joke but under the strain I failed to add that it was a tramcar, so the thing fell flat.

The 10.31 tram carried us to the pier, where I asked Wanda to sit on the beach until the arrival of the boat. By the remarks she made, she seemed to be under the impression that the *Queen Mary* could berth at Cudford Pier, whereas in actual fact she was destined to sail on a much smaller craft named *Queenie*.

This was the trickiest part of the day because Fred Collett hired his boats at five shillings per head, whereas all the money I possessed was six-and-six. Leaving Wanda to play the gramophone, I walked briskly to the far side of the pier and hired Fred Collett's best boat for five shillings. Then I rowed round the pier to where I had positioned Wanda out of Fred's fantastically sharp line of sight. I had played this game for years, though usually the party waiting for me on the far side of the Pier was five or six strong, enabling us to enjoy a day's outing for the modest outlay of one shilling per head. The secret was for all hands except the oarsman to lie flat until well out to sea, but how to ask Wanda to lie in the scuppers was a problem I preferred to exclude from my mind.

Wanda's pretty face registered unaccustomed displeasure at the sight of *Queenie.* "Surely we can't go all the way to Lark Island in that tiny cockleshell? It must be the dinghy for rowing me out to the cabin-cruiser you've hired for the day."

"Ha, ha! A cockleshell indeed! That's rich. All the more fun, Wanda—this way you really get the feel of the sea. Ha, ha!" A tactless remark in view of the amount of sea already slopping about in the bilge.

Wanda sat uncomfortably in the stern while I wielded the oars and stared at the long brown legs which oozed from beneath her green dress. Looking back, it seems madness that anyone in his right mind would head a rowboat for the open sea, with the intention of sculling clean over the horizon to a small island some six miles out in the English Channel, but in those days this was the kind of thing we did without a thought for danger. All that mattered was being alone with one's dream-girl, safe from the Marks, Simons and Richards of this highly-competitive world.

Carefully placing her dainty feet clear of the water, Wanda wound the magic box wherein Bing was waiting to warble *Pennies from Heaven* yet again. For some time now I had come to accept Bing as one of our crowd, always singing to us wherever we were or whatever we did, like a troubadour of old accompanying the nobles and their ladies. Nevertheless, I secretly wished on this particular occasion that he would climb out of the box and row for a change.

"That's *Pennies from Heaven,* isn't it, Wanda?" I small-talked, as though I hadn't heard it 70 times this summer.

"Yes, Peter. Do you love Bing as much as I do?"

"I like him on land; this is the first time I've heard him at sea."

Apparently I wasn't the only one who hadn't heard Bing at sea before, because on this close still morning I could distinctly hear fishermen a mile away remarking that trippers who frightened bass away might well get sunk. The heat of the sun made me remove my silk cravat and shirt, letting Wanda see the large muscles which were pulling her clear of civilization. If I was part of the eternal triangle, I had to show something to counteract Bing's vocal cords. Life was glorious, I thought to myself, and an occasion like this seemed the summit of human felicity.

Wanda discreetly removed her dress, now reclining astern in a sunsuit quite daring for that time. Never in my short life had I seen anybody so beautiful. She had acquired the golden tan of the advertisements, though not so golden as her hair, and her body had attained the transient perfection of sixteen. I searched her eyebrows, eyes, nose and lips for flaws without success. Even the chin was right, slightly cleft, rising to dimpled cheeks. Wanda had once called Marcus a Greek god. Nobody ever called me that. They could never get beyond such clichés as rugged or masculine, euphemisms for those with faces like Greek buses rather than gods. Wanda told me I was neither handsome nor ugly, but had been unable to specify where my countenance lay on this wide scale of pans. Her tone of voice clearly indicated buses.

Approximately half way across we tied up to a buoy so I could cool off in the sea while Wanda remained in the boat with Bing. As the soft waters caressed my body it struck me as unfortunate that of the three people on the trip I was the only one who did any rowing. I felt quite willing to sing, if only Bing would lend a hand with the oars for a spell. My appetite had returned, so I consoled myself with the knowledge that girls always took care of the refreshment side of excursions, as I looked longingly at Wanda's huge beach bag lying in the stern. For the past hour I had been studying the bag while rowing, whence the temptingly yellow tip of a banana protruded invitingly, like an omen of delicacies to come. I chaffed Wanda about the banana, whereupon she laughingly extracted it from the beach bag and squeezed it. A spray of talc fell mist-like on her lovely shoulders and she laughed, delightedly. "Isn't it just too cute, Peter? Simon gave it to me on my sixteenth birthday."

This incident led me to a foolish thought that although I had known Wanda all summer, never once had she eaten anything in my presence. Reminiscing further as I rowed, disclosed that never had I seen her drink, smoke, or even suck a sweet.

"Gosh, I'm peckish, Wanda," I grinned, as Lark Island beach gradually grew to reality ahead.

"Same here, Peter. It must be this glorious ozone. Looks like we shall be ready for an early lunch just as soon as we land."

My hopes rose as Wanda fumbled in the beach bag, only to sink again as she drew out a box-camera. She peered through the viewfinder at me, so I braced the muscles and turned on the personality smile for posterity.

"That won't do, Peter. I'm afraid you are in the way. Could you veer the boat slightly to starboard or whatever you call the right, so I can snap my very first sight of Lark Island?

"Ah, that's better but we're still too far off shore for detail.

Please row faster."

In order to please Wanda I pulled like a machine on a zigzag course, while she took photographs of the deserted beach and tree-fringed hinterland, until at last our keel slid gently on the sandy shore. Hot and weary, I noted I had been rowing almost non-stop for over two bours. Then an unexpected thing happened. I stepped out of the boat and fell full-length on the sand.

"Ha, ha!—I tripped and fell down," I laughed, as though it was an extremely difficult feat. Then I stood up, pretending to steady the skiff while Wanda disembarked, but really holding the gunwale for support. I was as weak as a puppy and trembling all over for lack of food. Wanda walked up the beach, then called me to carry Bing up too. I leaned over to do this and was amazed to find myself fall prostrate in the boat. I cursed myself for having eaten so little during the past week, sitting up in the boat to recoup my strength and figuring how best to carry the gramophone without crawling up the beach on my hands and knees.

The short rest gradually brought back my vigour, though not so markedly as my appetite. Wanda had spread a rug on the sand from the beach bag, upon which she reclined in the briefest of suits like a poster for Biarritz, already winding Bing so he could flood the island with mellifluous melody. A butterfly hovered round her head, as beautiful as a flying flower. This, I thought happily, was the moment I had dreamed of for so long— alone with Wanda on a glorious summer day. Aptly enough, Bing was crooning *Hawaiian Paradise,* and I nodded full agreement.

But soon Bing decided to mix love with nutrition, singing about the savoury smell of fried chicken, Southern style, smothered with all those delicious kidneys and potatoes my whole being craved. My saliva glands precluded speech until the disc ended, especially as Wanda was again fumbling in the beach bag. My heart sank to see her take out highly inedible binoculars, apparently for her hobby of bird-watching, but soon I was also scanning the trees and shore for bird life, though with an entirely different motive.

"Early lunch for me, dear," I suggested, lying as close to my beloved as the sweeping binoculars allowed. I had planned to make the big love play in this ideal setting, but to do so on an empty stomach was out of the question. At the moment I doubted whether my facial muscles could even pucker my lips for a kiss.

"Me too, Peter—I'm ravenous."

"Shall we eat right here?"

"Perfect! That suits me if it suits you."

What puzzled me was the way Wanda agreed with everything I said, yet made no effort to produce the picnic. Polite if nothing, I waited half an hour then said, "I wonder if you would mind changing the record, Wanda dear?" I made this request lest I be driven to attack the beach basket in desperation if Bing didn't quit singing his heart out about a midnight barbecue in lil' ole Montana with his honey, where the pair of them were preparing to celebrate their engagement by roasting an ox whole.

"Can I help you lay the table, dear?" I jested.

"Splendid idea, Peter. We'll do it properly and use my towel as our table-cloth."

I watched wide-eyed as Wanda pulled from the beach bag the biggest towel I had ever seen, and spread it over the sands like a multi-coloured carpet. The significant point was that now the beach bag lay there flat and empty. The association of ideas made me instinctively glance down at my stomach, to discover that it had completely disappeared from view. For the first time I realized the truth in the old expression of one's navel knocking against the backbone.

When Wanda had arranged the towel to her satisfaction

she said, "Perhaps you'd like to pop up and get the lunch now, Peter."

"Pop up where, dear?" Surely she didn't picture me as a hunting falcon, soaring up from the beach to strike my prey in mid air?"

"To the cafe, of course."

"What cafe?"

"Well, you know, the beach restaurant or whatever they call it here."

"But the island is uninhabited, dear. That's why I chose it for today. It's a bird sanctuary." Subconsciously I received a mental flash of myself gnawing a raw seagull.

"I wondered why there was nobody else in sight. That means we're stranded here with no food."

"I thought the girls always brought the . . . have you got anything to drink?"

"No, of course not, Peter. I was relying on you."

Suddenly it dawned on me that it was unlikely I could swallow food without liquid in my present dehydrated condition. Only Bing was unaffected by our deficiences, warbling away unconcernedly about the charms of his sweetie-pie over *Cocktails for Two.*

"So we're stuck on Lark Island without food or water, Wanda."

"Oh dear, what a shame. We'll have to go back to Cudford, that's all."

"But that means rowing! I just couldn't do it without a meal, dear."

"Then we'll search for shellfish. Won't that be fun! I've read that herring gulls drop mussels on rocks from a great height to open their shells."

"But I can barely walk, dear, let alone fly."

"All we need do is search around, and who knows but we'll find berries and perhaps a stream."

"Berries!" It was like offering a lion a pea for dinner.

We walked up the beach to the woods, then set off in different directions for the search. When Wanda was out of sight I sat on some grass and began unashamedly eating clover. I ended up with a mouthful of extremely unappetizing plant-life, almost impossible to swallow, so I abandoned the experiment. Finding nothing else even remotely edible I returned to the beach in search of meatier diet among the rocks. All the adventure stories I remembered always gave this as an abundant food source, but none of their heroes could ever have been stranded on Lark Island. Granted, there was sufficient seaweed to start an iodine factory and a plethora of crabs as big as shillings, but not a bite worth eating. How, I asked myself, did all these fat protected birds survive to bursting point where I couldn't collect as much as a snack?

Eventually Wanda returned with the good news that she had located a feast. This feast was contained in a handkerchief, from which she carefully counted out eighteen blackberries each. "These are all the ripe ones available, Peter," she explained, while I swallowed mine in one mouthful. "What did you find for lunch?"

Feeling far removed from Pook the hunter, I contributed a baby prawn which had drained every ounce of my stamina to catch, plus an unidentified shellfish whose casing was apparently constructed of tungsten steel. "Not much, I'm afraid, Wanda, and I can't even open the shellfish."

"Did you try dropping it from a great height onto a rock, like the birds do?"

"Better still, I dropped the rock on the shellfish, but still it won't open. The rock cracked."

Wanda smiled her wonderful smile. "Listen, Peter, let's stop worrying about food. After all, we're two adult people, so surely we can go a few hours without dying from hunger. It's fabulous to be away from the crowds for once, and this is such a fantastic setting that I'm going to lie here sunbathing and make the most of our wonderful day out together."

Wanda rubbed oil on her shoulders, back and legs, then wound the gramophone to bring Bing into the party. She stretched out her shapely body in repose, like a sea-goddess of old, while her faithful companion sent his voice rippling across the sands, informing us over and over again that nothing really mattered so long as we were both together, holding hands, kissing, and practically welded into one piece by the high-voltage attraction of love. In the course of his ballad Bing repeatedly referred to Wanda as his honey baby-mine, and as I surveyed this golden girl I could not but endorse his sentiments. Apart from never being bothered by such trivia of life as eating or rowing back to Cudford, Bing certainly reflected the dream world in which we seemed to live. The theme was always the idyllic love between a boy and a girl, something sacred which would grow with the years until one or the other followed the coffin at an incredibly advanced age, still madly in love with the deceased partner lying in the box. This was life as it was presented to us on records, radio, magazines and movies, so this was how we saw it.

I lay so close to Wanda that our bodies touched, while Bing catalogued the details of courtship in song, like a caller at a barn-dance. On the appropriate cue from Bing I gently took Wanda's hand in mine and bent over her. She had assumed the pose of blissful hypnotism under the rich voice of our tutor, and I was practically on top of her when Bing recommended me to steal a kiss on those rose-petal lips. I took his advice gladly, and my whole body quivered with excitement when Wanda returned the kiss with closed eyes—so feebly that she might have been a warrior dying on a desert battlefield. I awaited further instructions from the master, which followed in rapid succession. I pressed my lips to her eyelids, tickled her nose and whispered "I love you, darling," mouthing the words deeply in my chest to obtain Bing's rich resonance.

Wanda murmured "I love you too, darling," just as Bing had predicted, and involuntarily I looked up at the gramohone to see if Bing was watching us. On the second chorus I repeated the process in every detail, except that I said "I love you, darling," so low that I reminded myself of Big Ben striking the hour, hot with passion and forgetful even of hunger. But there was a sense of let-down because Bing always ended his lesson at that point. Where did one go from here? I racked my brains to recall all his records we knew well, in search of the advanced course I needed so badly. The master danced, wined and dined his ladies, held their hands, stole kisses, thought about them for days afterwards, even carried torches for years —and once suddenly referred to the patter of tiny feet, following the insistent peal of church bells and the good offices of the preacher man— but there was never any reference to the vital inbetween stage. Perhaps there were other crooners who filled this gap for enthusiastic adolescents but they were not on Wanda's record list.

At such close quarters I observed Wanda's beauty as never before. Despite the occasional inconvenience of the blackberries, which rattled inside me as though I had swallowed ball-bearings, I daringly kissed this goddess once more, and again she weakly returned the kiss. Where was the passion of love we learned at the movies, I asked myself disappointedly, where sweethearts embraced like well-matched wrestlers?

Wanda rubbed her soft cheek against mine, whispering softly in my ear the words I longed to hear. "Would you do me just one little favour, Peter?"

"Gladly, darling. You know I'd do anything in the world for you. Anything."

"Please put on another record, Peter, but change the needle first, there's a pet."

Smiling falsely, I went through the familiar process without leaving Wanda's side. If we married, would our honeymoon be like this, with Bing ever at the bedside serenading my bride for me at one-and-threepence a time?

"I wonder what Brian and Helen are doing now?" Wanda remarked, as Bing went right back to square one by spotting his honey for the very first time as she ran out of the High School gates.

Automatically I glanced along the beach to see if the crowd were arriving. "They said they were going to take a picnic lunch to Roker Beach," I replied gloomily. The picture was clear in my mind—Brian and Helen wolfing the victuals while Bing sang to them from another little box. Then Helen would say to Brian, "I wonder where Wanda and Peter are today?" and Brian would reply, "They said they were going over to Lark Island."

Wanda yawned genteely. "What a pity we didn't think to make a foursome, Peter."

"But there wouldn't have been room in the boat, dearest."

"No, I mean we could have all gone to Roker Beach. Brian said he hoped to borrow his father's car."

Stifling an upsurge of jealousy I made a mental resolution to obtain a car somehow, and, above all things, learn to croon. I was utterly fed up with Bing doing my courting for me. Sliding an arm round Wanda's waist I whispered, "I'd rather be here alone with you, Bing—I mean, Wanda."

"We should have brought the beach ball, Peter, then we could have had fun on the sands."

"Not on an empty stomach, dear. We've got to get back yet."

"Oh dear, what a horrid thought."

"What, leaving our little island and going back to all those crowds?"

"No, rowing all those tedious miles across the sea."

"Oh."

Life with Wanda was not the orgy of boiling passion I had hoped, for it seemed incongruous that so desirable a maiden should be so unresponsive.

"Before we leave, Peter, there's one special thing I'd love to do. Are you game to help me, now there's not a soul about to see us."

"Of course, darling. Just name it and I'm your willing slave." So it had come at last, I exulted within me.

"Oh, good! I want you to pose on the rug while I take a photograph of you for my album."

For the first time in my life I felt too weak and dispirited to pose. Instead, I lay on the rug as though my body had been washed ashore from a wreck. I heard Wanda say "Cheese, please," but just as my mind grappled with the savoury word, my eyes looked seaward. Suddenly I sat up in dismay, because our boat was where we had left it but the sea had gone. Between the boat and the lapping waves was a yellow stretch of sand some hundred yards in length, and the tide was still ebbing fast.

"We're high and dry, Wanda," I gasped, falling back on the rug in despair.

"Oh, so we are. Never mind, Peter, my brother Paul told me how strong you are, so you'll soon be able to pull the boat across the sand—it's all wet and slippery."

"Listen, Wanda, you'll have to give me a hand, but first I'll try to find a log or something to act as a roller."

I searched in vain for a log on this cursed island which yielded nothing to intruders like me, but on the tide-mark was a small plank of sufficient bulk to provide a fulcrum for sliding the keel. Using this, we heaved the boat towards the sea as best we could, slowly and laboriously, until Wanda made the cruel suggestion that I carry the skiff on my head, as I had done with the club boat. "Otherwise, Peter, I'm afraid the tide is going out faster than we are moving the boat." Hearing this terrifying idea, I bared my teeth and dragged the craft like a madman until at last it floated in the water. Then I fell helpless in its bottom, exhausted beyond telling.

When eventually I opened my eyes Wanda was sitting in the stern, trailing a hand through the water. "You are sleepy today, Peter. We've been popping along on the tide quite comfortably, so I didn't wake you."

I peered over the gunwale, to find the boat was drifting rapidly out of the cove on the ebb tide towards home. This sight so heartened me that I managed to sit on the thwart and commence short easy strokes with the oars. "We'll be home in no time at this rate, Wanda."

"The first thing I shall do is to eat everything in our larder," she laughed, switching on Bing to sing us on our way. This time he was in more sentimental mood, watching red sails in the sunset and praying the evening breeze would blow his loved one right into his outstretched arms as he waited for her on the beach. To pass the time I imagined myself as Wanda's husband, filling our little cottage with melody as I sang to her that the kettle was boiling and soon she would have tea in bed from the hands of her beloved, this morning and every morning till eternity.

Once we were clear of the cove a refreshing wind sprang up. From my seat amidships Lark Island seemed to be moving slowly sideways as it receded, then after a few minutes the sideways movement quickened. "Strong current out here, Wanda," I said, pulling strongly on the sculls. "Difficult to hold her on our direct course."

Wanda looked astern and saw that the island was rapidly moving westwards instead of southwards. "Row harder, Peter. We seem to be carried along sideways."

I was now pulling as if competing in a regatta but there was no hiding the fact that in some unaccountable fashion both of us could see the island without looking back, for it was directly on our port beam. "I'm afraid the current is too strong for us, Wanda. It's taking us round the eastern shore, so we'd better row back to the island and wait for the tide to turn."

I headed the bow for shore and rowed vigorously, but the island continued to slide sideways instead of nearer. "Never mind, Wanda, we'll soon be in the lee of the island and land on the south shore."

"Which side did we sunbathe on, Peter?"

"The north beach, facing the mainland."

"Oh dear! We must be going round the island."

Twenty minutes of really hard pulling convinced me we had seen the last of Lark Island, let alone the south beach. Not only was it impossible to make headway against the current, but the fresh wind turned our bow away from land no matter how strongly I heaved on the port sweep. Worst of all, Lark Island began to diminish in size by the minute, and I felt so exhausted and starved that I feared I might faint in front of Wanda.

"Why aren't we getting any nearer the island, Peter?"

"I'm afraid the boat is being swept past it, dear. Sorry, but there's nothing more I can do about it." I felt sorely tempted to ask her to bring Bing out to lend a hand, but he had retreated into the shelter of his box, waiting for better times.

"Where are we now, Peter?"

"We're out in the English Channel, dear, but don't worry —someone is bound to sight us and pick us up."

Quite unexpectedly Wanda began to cry, and her action prevented me doing the same thing. By now the island was a blur in the distance, with nothing else but the great circle of horizon around us. On the southern rim of the circle, some minutes later, appeared the hazy outline of a liner which I identified as the *Queen Mary*. I optimistically waved an oar, as though her lookout could possibly spot us over such vast distance.

"Where will the current take us, Peter?" Wanda sobbed, childlike.

"Well, France, of course, so we're quite safe, but please don't worry—we're bound to be sighted before then."

"The *Queen Mary* didn't see us."

"Because she was all of eight miles away—but that proves we're drifting towards the main shipping lanes. They sail up and down there like buses in Oxford Street."

"But it will be dark by then and we may get run down."

"Oh, we'll be picked up long before that."

I kept telling myself this was a ghastly nightmare, and it was only a matter of time before I woke up safe in my bed at home. Foolishly I wondered what Bing would do in a situation like this. Perhaps he would sing a sea-shanty about being alone with his cutie-pie on the ocean of love, wishing he could drift like this with her in his arms for ever and ever, whatever the weather, come rain, come shine. I knew that if I consulted him on the subject right now, he would tell me in irrepressible song that any time is loving time, with your honey's cheek next to yours, the moon above and the ocean all around you.

I sat there appalled by the danger of the situation, and stupified by the thought that my wonderful date with Wanda had ended by being adrift in a dinghy with her in the English Channel. Two merchant ships passed, so far over the horizon that we could scarcely see them, let alone be seen.

But about 7.30 a smaller vessel hove in sight, on a course much nearer our own position. Excitedly I waved the oar non-stop until it was clear we had been spotted, then awaited rescue with a sense of relief so strong as to be almost akin to pain. By now we could discern the craft as a small cabin-cruiser, and even at that distance the rich and reassuring voice of Bing wafted across the water to us, informing the world that he was sitting in a small Spanish café, gazing into his honey's eyes through candlelight while guitars serenaded them as their hands touched across the table for two. Instinctively I looked at Wanda's box, wondering by what miracle Bing had left it in order to bring help in our hour of distress.

From the deck Brian and Helen waved to us, and behind them an older Brian was visible at the wheel of the craft, whom I knew to be Brian's rich father. Brian was hailing us: "Pater picked us up off Roker Beach. Thought we'd like a trip in his new forty-footer. Helen said 'I wonder how Peter and Wanda are getting on at Lark Island,' so pater said 'Let's go and find out'—so here we are. Sorry to butt in, Peter, but do you fancy a tow back or something?—you're slightly off course for Cudford, unless Wanda is eloping with you to Normandy."

"We're in need of everything, Brian, from a tow to food. Can you come alongside and take us on board? Oh, Wanda, what a godsend we're safe at last!"

It is extraordinary how quickly people, especially young people, can pass from crisis to normality. Within twenty minutes the four of us were squatting on a rug, spread amidships, with *Queenie* safely in tow aft, telling of our exploits on Lark Island and devouring the remains of Brian's picnic lunch, while Bing sang to us from his little box as though he knew everything would turn out all right in the end.

Wanda was asking, "Did you see Doreen and Richard when you were at Roker Beach, Helen?"

"No, I met them yesterday and they said they would probably be going over to Yalton Cove for the day. But we did see Rosemary. She was wearing her new cerise swimsuit."

"Was Simon with her?"

"Not at the time, but she said she had arranged to meet him this afternoon for tea."

"I saw Simon yesterday but he didn't mention anything about going to Roker Beach or meeting Rosemary. Did you know about it, Peter?"

"No, Wanda, except that Patricia and Norman were

planning to go there as well."

"Never mind, we're bound to meet them tomorrow, so we'll find out if Simon came after all. . . ."

As we sped smoothly homeward in the warm evening air, lighted by an enormous orange sun floating on the horizon, Bing's sonorous baritone confirmed that all was well once more in the world of young lovers.

SIX

Courting Wanda was such a strain on the mind that I gladly accepted Alec's suggestion that we take out a couple of normal girls for field operations, as he put it in his down-to-earth manner. Nobody can wear their Sunday suit every day of the week, he added, so we should look for more ordinary girls who would enjoy the thrill of our company. This was Alec's crafty way of meeting Brandy, who, for some inexplicable feminine reason, refused to go out unless accompanied by her friend Olga.

Brandy had gained her unusual nickname the previous Christmas, when we had taken the girls to a pub, the Bricklayer's Arms, for a drink to celebrate the holiday. Alec always bought everybody one drink at Christmas, taking their orders with great care—such as gins, sherries, vodkas, whiskies, and so on—then returning from the bar with a tray full of halves of mild for them, without a word of explanation. However, on this occasion Brandy refused to be duped, returning herself to the bar and having the landlord change her half of mild for a brandy, as she had ordered. Hearing the price, Alec made elaborate pantomime of falling off his chair as the result of heart failure, to lie motionless on the floor as if struck dead by terrible news. Our circumstances in those days were so impecunious that we gathered round the body in noisy sympathy, using some of the brandy to revive Alec—half amused by his performance, half alarmed that perhaps such unexpected extravagance really had rendered him unconscious.

Although she was never again to violate our rule about spirits, Brandy had earned herself a new name that was to stick for good.

Taking out Brandy and Olga was an operation more complicated than one might suppose. The most important thing was to borrow the car from Alec's brother. This relic of pioneer motoring was a vintage Austin Seven, constructed on the lines of a large pram without a hood, purchased in the open market for the remarkably reasonable sum of thirty shillings plus a pair of ice-skates. We pushed the Austin round to Cyril's garage for the usual nightly service of half a gallon of petrol for one shilling—a pint of free oil from Cyril's tank of sump drainings; water for the radiator and air for the tyres. We inflated the tyres to near solidity, at 45 pounds to the square inch, which enabled us to motor all evening before they eventually went flat. There was no such luxury on the Austin as a petrol gauge, but this omission was overcome by the use of a bean-stick measuring rod and the knowledge that our half gallon guaranteed a run of twenty miles. If we ran out of fuel en route we cheerfully pushed the car home as one would a heavy hand-cart.

On completing the service and paying Cyril one shilling for the petrol, Alec sat in the car while I pushed it round to Hill Lane, the road in which Brandy lived, in order to save fuel. I sometimes thought that Alec's affections first fell on Brandy because she resided in a road which boasted a 1 in 12 gradient, ideal for free-wheeling the Austin until its brave little engine fired. Arriving at the home of his beloved, Alec's first duty was to produce a special accessory for the front wheel in order to reinforce the ancient braking system, known to the layman as a brick. This essential equipment lay in the centre of our coiled tow-rope, beside the bean-stick dip rod and the red oil-lamp Alec had found by a road excavation site in Cudford Crescent. The lamp served as a parking light, and sometimes as a warning to the motoring public that once again the Austin had run dry too far out in the country to be pushed home.

Clad in the fashion of the day Brandy high-heeled her way to the car, giving one the impression that her knees were handcuffed together. Alec stood waiting to lift her in, because girls wearing tight skirts had to be admitted thus for the doors had long since dropped off and Alec had been obliged to weld sheet metal across the apertures in order to prevent passengers unexpectedly leaving the vehicle when cornering at speed. Having lifted Brandy in and arranged her legs so that they did not interfere with the gear-lever, Alec welcomed her with a kiss, then nodded to me to remove the brick and jump in.

Although the Austin boasted a back seat, there were no foot-wells, so I sat sideways as though travelling on a shelf. This sufficed until we picked Olga up, when it was necessary to lift her into the back seat and tuck her long legs under her, so she resembled a travelling Buddha. When darkness fell Olga usually sat with her legs on my lap but she considered this pose too immodest by day. Passing motorists must have thought I was some kind of giant, because I had to sit on top of our tow-rope, a position which engraved such intricate herringbone patterns on my bottom that Alec suggested the latter should go on public exhibition as Modern Art. The picnic basket reposed in the sole remaining space, under Olga's bust.

"Where are we going today, Wonder Boy?" Brandy inquired, as if she refused to accept the inevitability of life.

Alec grinned, as though springing a surprise treat on us. "Down to the River Cud, darling, where it flows by Farmer Telford's meadow. It's nice and woody there and no crowds."

"One thing about you, Alec—you're not the fickle type. You certainly stick to what you know. By now we should have squatters' rights on that spot."

The chief advantage of the Cud was its distance from home, nine and a half miles, making it the perfect rendezvous for paupers whose excursions were based on half gallons of petrol, leaving a safety margin of one mile for head-winds.

"Far enough, Brandy. I'm happy just being with you. Distance couldn't make it better." Alec had once hinted he loved Brandy so much that he would be equally content picnicking in her back garden.

Always short of cash, we set out on these trips without

sweets, cigarettes or drink. As a result none of us smoked, but Alec now produced a cigarette-like object which he stuck in his mouth and lit with as much care as one would ignite a bonfire.

"I've been experimenting with rhubarb leaves mixed with saltpetre," he explained, to account for the smell and tiny explosions at each drag. In his ceaseless search for the poor man's tobacco, Alec was working his way through his garden, from dock leaves to dried mint. The cigarette was passed round the four of us as though we were drug addicts.

"Much better than parsley, but still vile," Brandy decided.

"So glad you like it, dear, because I've rolled twenty for us."

Alec drove the Austin with superb skill, as indeed he had to if it was to carry such a load through the hills of Cudfordshire to the river. To save gas he drove on the principle that the brake was a refinement not yet invented, free-wheeling down slopes to gain maximum mileage. On steep up-gradients I leaped out and pushed, helping the engine and saving weight in one operation. Alec always ended the journey as though he was going to drive us straight into the River Cud, bouncing over the grass and shrieking "Help! The steering's packed up!" As ever, he managed to turn at the last moment and save his terrified passengers.

While Olga and Brandy laid the rug for the picnic, Alec and I undressed prior to plunging into the water to inspect the fish, as he put it. The girls considered this sport too dangerous, especially since Alec disappeared one day over the weir, to return later on foot looking extremely sorry for himself.

Tea was always the same; four rock-cakes and thermos-flask tea which tasted flat and celluloidy consumed in apparent rapture. After the meal we men leaned back, smoking Alec's herbal cigarettes and trying to look as though we enjoyed such a revolting experience, while the girls cuddled up to us waiting to be loved.

"I'm not ready to woo yet," Alec told Brandy. At the moment he was so obsessed by his rhubarb experiment that even Brandy had temporarily lost some of her glamour.

Olga melted into my arms as she had learned from the movies, determined to have her share of the welter of romance hosed over us by the films and records. Bing was unable to join us on these excursions solely because there just wasn't room in the Austin for his little morocco-bound home.

Kissing Olga was quite an experience, rather like pressing one's lips into a cosmetic display-counter, making you realize how it was impossible for her to join us in the river without dyeing the waters. Her lavish use of eye make-up gave her the startled appearance of one who sees a ghost behind you, enhanced by the deathly pallor of face-powder. The whiteness was relieved by two cheeks rouged to assimilate localized scarlet fever, but the most conspicuous feature of her pretty face was the mouth. The Cupid's bow effect had gone out of fashion, to be replaced by what Alec called Cupid's suction-cup. Olga's film heroines favoured large sensual lips like curved sausages, so she copied them by painting her own generous lips even larger than life with a kind of crimson candle which coloured everything it touched, including her pretty teeth. Again from the movies, Olga had developed a habit of apparently passing away in her sleep when being kissed—a swoon of passion so convincing that when she first performed it I foolishly inserted her vanity mirror in her mouth, thinking she had died in my arms.

At the moment she was in the passive pose of expectancy, her startled eyes closed to reveal blue eyelids fringed with Woolworth's long lashes. The outsize lips were pursed and slightly open in feminine surrender, while the gentle heaving of the bosom told me she was still breathing.

"Kiss me, Peter," she whispered, motionless as a ventriloquist.

I looked about me to see who had spoken, then realizing it must have been Olga practising her new art of talking despite facial paralysis. I took a deep breath like a pearl-diver, in readiness for amorous exercise. Part of Olga's new technique was to lose control of her jaw muscles, letting her mouth drop open as though I was a shortsighted dentist, until I was forced to support it with my free hand. This precaution when kissing her was necessary ever since Alec had warned me about the risk of my falling in, and the advisability of wearing boots as a safety measure against complete engulfment. Tenderly closing Olga's mouth—which Alec facetiously referred to in conversation as visiting the Cheddar Caves—I kissed my beloved's lips with the eagerness of youth.

In contrast to kissing a corpse, Alec and Brandy kissed like small boys wrestling on grass. In our adolescent exploration in the world of sex Alec and I had already made a secret pact that as soon as opportunity offered we would change partners, so I could sample the joys of dynamic love-making while Alec tried his luck with my lifeless virgin.

"Or perhaps she's drugged," Alec had suggested when we compared notes.

"Drugged my foot! It's all those movies she sees, where the heroine faints every time she goes into a clinch. No wonder they used to beat women in the old days—it was the only way to get any action."

"Why don't you kiss her standing up?"

"Then I'd have to carry her back to the car."

"Well, try throwing a bucket of water over her to wake her up. Brandy needs that to cool her off. Of course, it may be you, Peter."

"What do you mean by a remark like that?"

"Perhaps you have that effect on women. They take one look at your face and go unconscious."

It was while I was clamping the lifeless body of Olga in

my arms, to dip my lips into her make-up till my own face turned red, that I saw it. I stared a long time at the woods fringing the river bank to ensure that the nearness of Olga's shapely body was not tricking my senses. I had never seen a raw elephant anywhere before, let alone in the beautiful Cudfordshire countryside, so the spectacle really startled me. I whispered to Alec, "Don't make a fuss and startle the girls, but take a shufti behind you and then tell me if that's an elephant over there—or a haystack with legs."

Alec whose keen eyes could spot a blonde at a thousand yards, pressed Brandy's face to his chest and peered inland. He shook his head as one who has seen a vision, then turned to me.

"Three, Peter, and don't let's kid ourselves they're oversized cows with tails at each end. Lie quiet and they may go away."

We both stared spellbound as three elephants slowly ambled in our direction. Then Alec's eyes were wide, as his mouth formed the word *seven* for me to see. I stared back at him in horror and elaborately mouthed my own estimate of ten. Alec signalled with the fingers of his free hand until I had read twelve.

Open-mouthed, we watched a dozen elephants of varying sizes tramp ponderously through the undergrowth, but now there was no mistaking their direction. They were heading straight for us.

Instinctively I clamped a hand over Olga's generous mouth and tried to say casually "Don't panic, dear, but I think we'd better move. There's a herd of elephants coming this way."

Olga's stifled scream aroused Brandy, who looked over Alec's shoulder and shrieked so harrowingly that Alec remarked something about getting her a job on the front of a fire-engine as a siren. In an instant we were holding the girls' hands and scampering along the bank. Alec panted, "Find some cover fast—I've read that elephants can outpace a horse when they really get going. Please don't scream any more, Brandy—you may stampede them."

Girls in tight skirts and stiletto heels are not the best companions for jungle flight, so we soon found ourselves huddled behind the frail cover of the Austin Seven, watching in bewilderment as a dozen elephants moved over the ground and into the river like an African safari scene we had witnessed so often at the movies.

"Look, it's Tarzan of the Apes!" Brandy screamed, as a muscular, half-naked man appeared through the trees holding a stick. "Oh, isn't he just too beautiful—look at his muscles! I can't bear it!"

It seemed remarkable that even Brandy—ardent lover of mankind—could forget danger so quickly at the sight of a male. This sunburnt giant with the face of a statue-god turned and frightened us all with a call of remarkable power to the woods behind him.

"He is Tarzan!" Brandy sighed ecstatically. "I expect he's telling the lions to hurry up."

"Lions! We've been coming here for ages and never seen anything more vicous than a water vole."

Olga cried, "If he's Tarzan I wish I could be his mate. Goodness! There's another Tarzan coming through the trees. Brandy, just look at his dinky little shorts. Oh, he's lovely!" Alec and I winced as Brandy pronounced both Tarzans to be sweet. Several elephants were now sporting in the water, and I noticed how the river seemed to be full of marker buoys floating across the stream. I was just about to tell the girls of my interesting discovery when yet another marker buoy splashed heavily from the rear of the leading elephant, so I shut up.

The first Tarzan shouted over to us, "Do not be in fear—we come only to wash our elephants."

"Sounds like Cudford Laundry," Alec remarked.

"Come across and see, if you wish. There is no danger from the animals."

Alec whispered to me, "He's right—the danger comes from him and his mate. Just look at those girls."

Brandy and Olga were running over the turf in that awkward gait of girls obsessed by elephants—knees together, feet out and arms like wings.

"Are you really Tarzan, Tarzan?" Brandy crooned, gulping in the muscle display. "I've seen every picture you ever made. Oh, Olga, isn't it just too thrilling!"

"No, no, I am not Tarzan Tarzan. I am Carlo, and this is my brother Nicholi. So, you beautiful maidens come to help us wash our elephants, yes?"

"Oh, yes, rather, please."

Alec said, "Peter and I will just stand here and iron them for you when they're dry."

"'Do you lovely men live in Cudford Forest then?" Brandy cried, as one who has seen a vision.

"No, no, we live in Spain."

"And you come all that way to wash your elephants?"

"Ah, we are washing our elephants here because this is the nearest river to our camp. At home we are washing our elephants in the River Tagus. Perhaps you and your bewitching friend would care to ride an elephant, yes?"

"Oh, we daren't, would we, Olga?

"Ah, I shall be with you to see no harm is coming to you."

"Oh, yes please!"

Alec and I watched in silent astonishment as the girls kicked off their shoes, while Carlo had a quick word with one of the herd in Spanish. The huge beast agreed to the proposition and knelt down so Carlo and Nicholi could lift the girls upon its back.

"Shall I fetch some newspaper?" Alec shouted worriedly, but the girls ignored him. "Funny thing about women, Peter;

they won't sit in your car unless there's a week's newspapers between their dresses and the upholstery, yet they don't mind squatting on a smelly great elephant with a hide like rubberized mud."

Carlo jumped on the head of the beast, Nicholi on the rump, with the two girls between them. Brandy clutched Carlo round the waist with her head resting on his hairy chest, informing the herd that if she had to be killed at least she'd die happy. Olga clamped Nicholi in similar fashion, screaming with delight as the elephant slowly rose and ambled into the river. I noticed how Olga's face bore the expression of one who has entered Paradise at an early age, and is determined to get her money's worth of bliss.

"You may become a little damp, carissima," Carlo was telling Brandy as the elephant sent up a fountain of water from its trunk, apparently under the impression that its passengers were on fire.

"Who's carissima—me?"

"But of course—in the language of love it is meaning my dearest one."

"I thought at first you meant the elephant. Oh, I don't mind the water one little bit; it's such fun, and so cooling."

An odd remark from a girl who regarded rain as damaging to clothes as sulphuric acid.

Alec remarked to me gloomily, "The best thing I can do is flog the car and buy a blooming elephant. How else can you compete with these male nudes?"

Carlo hailed us to join in the fun. "Come, young men, have no fear. Choose an elephant and mount his back. This is all you need."

Apparently all we needed were two ordinary garden brooms, which were used for scrubbing the massive hides as one would sweep a pavement. Alec and I sulkily chose our beasts, who immediately moved out into the river, boat fashion, ready for their toilet.

"They like you to sing to them while you work, lads," Carlo called across.

"Scrub-a-dub-dub, scrub-a-dub-dub," Alec sang unenthusiastically, as he plied the broom on Fatima. "Scrub-a-dub-dub, scrub-a-dub-dub, too big for a tub, so they bath in the Cud."

Fatima showed her musical appreciation by curling her trunk and hosing Alec clean off her back in one graceful motion. Everybody laughed except Alec, whose fag had been broken by another marker buoy floating close at hand.

At the end of the half-hour session the girls were soaked but happy, Olga declaring it to be the most thrilling day of her life since she had once accidentally strayed into the changing-room of Cudford Rugby Club immediately after the match, when thirty of her heroes were under the showers.

"Come with me, my pretty maids, and dry your clothes in our caravan," Carlo suggested.

It was quite nauseating the way the girls shrieked at every-thing the brothers said, as though they were being tickled unexpectedly with feathers.

"A caravan! You live in a real caravan!" Brandy shrilled.

"But of course, pretty one. All members of Farrango's Circus are doing this thing."

"Farrango's Circus! You actually work in a circus! Oh, please show us your caravan."

"We'd better come too, in case it needs scrubbing," Alec remarked sourly.

"No, my friend—it is more wise you stay here with Peter and guard the elephants. Nicholi and I will bring back the girls by car, thus saving time. If necessary, we will wrap them in our blankets."

It was the strangest situation of my life, sitting on the banks of the Cud we knew so well, in charge of twelve elephants from Farrango's Circus. "What do you make of this lot?" I asked Alec, who was using Fatima as a windbreak to light a rhubarb cigarette to steady his nerves.

"All I can suggest, Peter, is follow the old adage—when in doubt consult the law. It's coming up behind you right now."

Cycling along the towpath was that one-man Interpol in the shape of Constable Barrington, whom Alec once described as not so much a man as a mob.

"Ho, ho, what have we here then, O Hannibal of the Alps?" he called, in the flat voice of one who has experienced every vagary of behaviour in the human race.

"Oh, that's a car, Constable; better known to you as the horseless carriage. Do draw up an elephant and sit down."

"Ho, ho, so we're still as saucy as ever, eh, Pook? I refers, of course, to them outsize beasts mucking up our river there. And for gawdsake don't tell me you thought they was trout with legs."

"Oh, those. Alec mentioned them just now when they landed here. He reckons they're pigeons from outer space. Don't take any notice and they'll fly off in a minute. They're probably after the cake crumbs we left from tea."

"Don't come the clevercuts with me, Pook. What I wants to know is why you're lounging about down here, tending an 'erd of blessed great elephants on common land like you was part-time shepherds or something."

"All right, Constable, you've caught us red-handed, so let's have the handcuffs. We were deprived as children, so we pinched twelve elephants from Geary's Pet Shop in the High Street."

"You ain't deprived, Pook—you're depraved. Just you come clean or I'll book you for causing an obstruction on a public towpath and foulin' up the river with effluent."

"And exercising animals without a lead as well."

"All right, Pook, have it your own way, but would the

aforesaid beasts be anything to do with Farrango's Circus across to Farmer Telford's meadow?"

"A circus? Who's ever heard of elephants in a circus, Constable? Surely you're kidding."

"Maybe I am, but I sees two half-naked foreigners taking your birds into a fancy trailer just now, so I says to meself, ho, ho, Pook and partner must be in the vicinity somewheres, and they must have done a tidy old swop for our Olga and Brandy. Now I finds you traded 'em for a dozen assorted mammals. You gone into the white slave traffic on the side, Pook? You knows as well as me that you can't keep them brutes in your backyard. They needs half a ton of hay just for elevenses."

"All right, Constable, Carlo and Nicholi will soon be back with the girls," I replied, alarmed about the caravan possibilities. "We're just minding the elephants while Olga and Brandy dry their clothes."

"Ho, ho!—drying their clothes, eh? That's a good 'un. Last time we had a case of a girl drying her clothes was down to Makton's Family Fair last Easter. She dried her clothes all right—and got in the family way at the same time. You're stuck out here with their elephants while they're in the caravan with your birds. You must be even thicker than I gave you credit for, Pook. If I let you mind my bike Saturday, can I borrow Olga for the night?"

For once I declined badinage with Constable Barrington because Alec and I were already streaking westwards as fast as our legs could carry us, in the hope of saving the girls from the Spanish Armada even at this late hour.

SEVEN

Dr Windebank, our Headmaster, adjusted his gown and peered through gold pince-nez at the foolscap careers form lying on his desk. "So, Pook, having almost completed five years of what are euphemistically known as educational pursuits, do you yourself feel confident that you emerge from our Alma Mater sufficiently qualified to take your rightful place in society on the dole?"

Sitting awkwardly in Dr Windebank's study for the customary careers' interview was not my conception of the summit of human felicity.

"Not quite, sir."

"Ah well, you may be right. Your class results show that you have not quite attained to that degree of academic eminence necessary for the enjoyment of Public Assistance, though it must be said in your favour that you have soared above those qualifications essential for a grant from the state as a mentally handicapped person. Let us see what your record shows: Captain of House Football, Vice-Captain of School Football, Captain of House Boxing, Captain of School Boxing, Green Belt Award for Judo, Captain of House Athletics, School Colours for Cornish Wrestling, a First in Unarmed Combat, a Second in Weight-lifting. What's this?—Commended for Tossing the Caber, whomsoever he may be. One presumes that any moment now and we shall come to your academic qualifications. Anchor in Tug-o-War Team, Colours for Fencing, Highly Commended for Quarterstaff, School Record for Throwing the Cricket Ball. . . . Good heavens, man, is that all you have to show after five years of the best educational facilities this country has to offer?"

"Oh no, sir—I won the Thor Shield last year."

"For your Latin studies?"

"I'm afraid not, sir. It was awarded for Throwing the Hammer."

"And did you hit him?"

"Who, sir?"

"Our Metalwork master. One naturally assumes you threw the hammer during Metalwork session."

"Oh no, sir, we aren't allowed to aim at teachers. I threw it during Field Events."

"But surely you have something in the academic field to counterbalance this welter of physical endeavour? A prospective employer may well deduce that he is hiring a professional gladiator straight from the Colosseum at Rome. I visualize you presenting yourself for interview accompanied by lions."

"I can always say I was top in woodwork, sir. I sawed through a four-inch plank in a minute and a half, end to end."

"Therefore one can only assume that for the first time in its long history, dating back to 1597, Cudford Grammar School has produced a chippy."

"Oh no, sir, I don't want to be a chippy."

"Well, that's some consolation at least. On what profession have you set your sights—no matter how low its trajectory?"

"I want to be a professional boxer, sir."

"A professional boxer! A prize-fighter, a common pugilist, a leather merchant, as I read in the popular press!"

"A professor of slugology, sir, or a chartered mitt-slinger— that will sound better on the College Valedictory Roll, sir."

Dr Windebank began to puff as though he was tiring rapidly in a six-round eliminator. "No, my boy, we of Cudford Grammar School are justly proud of our contribution to the professions and the Universities, but we have never—and shall never— subscribe to Casey's Gym. What is your alternative choice of career?"

"It's listed on the form, sir—there at the bottom. Professional footballer. Portsmouth F.C. If full up, try Arsenal. As last resort, would consider Chelsea."

Dr Windebank wiped his brow puzzledly. "These are

obviously youthful fancies, Pook. I myself recall as a schoolboy having wild dreams of becoming a music-hall juggler. Now, to bring our conversation to a more practical level, have you thought about the Navy?"

"Constantly, sir."

"And what conclusion did you arrive at?"

"They guard the mighty deep, sir. I've thought about the Army too, sir."

"With what result?"

"They guard the land, sir."

"I will refrain from askng you who guards the air, Pook, lest you inform me it is the National Association of Barbers. What I am driving at is do you wish to join the Navy?"

"I've never thought about that, sir."

"Well, for heaven's sake think about it now."

"Frankly, sir, the Navy's not for me."

"Why not, pray?"

"Even if I prayed, I wouldn't fancy the Navy, sir."

"For what good reason?"

"They don't have professional boxers, sir—only amateurs.'"

"What an extraordinary young man you are, to be sure. As a matter of interest to a mere layman, tell me, Pook, how do you intend to become a professional boxer?"

"By fighting for money, sir."

"I see. Have you yet made a start on this highly unsavoury career?"

"Well, sir, so far I've always fought for love, but next week I'm working—that's the way we talk of fighting in the trade out of town. They've given me a bout with Fireman Tucker of Southampton. They call me the Cudford Infant."

"What will be your starting salary?"

"£5 for a win, sir."

"What do you receive if you lose?"

"A thundering good hiding, sir. No good losing in this game. Tucker's a nasty bit of work who's due to get done over. All his mates think he's unbeatable, so naturally it's up to me to put them right. He's not a ladder-and-squirt fireman, sir, but a coal-slinger aboard a ferry-boat. They open the furnace door and he bungs it in with a shovel—that sort of fireman. All bung and no brain."

"I am aware of the difference, Pook, without your drawing a diagram to explain it. How old is this brainless bunger of coal?"

"Eighteen, sir. He can't go any higher in his profession unless he takes the Board of Trade exams. If he passes, they let him open the furnace door on his own. We're billed for a six-round preliminary, but with my alert mind I reckon to stiffen him in three."

Dr Windebank closed my file with a sigh. "I think it would be well, Pook, if you did not publicize this deplorable exhibition about the school. We are told today that the young are lacking in initiative and the old spirit of adventure, so go to Southampton and take your chance. Then return here with some more stable and respectable ideas in the way of a career. Good-day to you."

Fireman Tucker's reputation was really based on two physical attributes, a heavy right hand and a magnificently developed mouth which never tired of telling you about his favourite topic—Fireman Tucker. Owing to the cramped accommodation at the Dockers and Lightermen's Hall it was necessary for me to change in the same toilet as my opponent, who, characteristically, began to needle me the moment I entered wearing my straw boater. Realizing the importance of publicity, I always wore the straw boater as a kind of trade-mark, right into the ring, removing it only when the bell sounded for the first round. I made a point of raising it politely to the crowd when they booed me, as well as to the referee and my opponent when we were introduced. The sight of a man in boxing kit with a straw boater on his head tickled the crowd immensely and ensured that my picture was in all the papers next day, above such naive captions as *The Fighting Milliner.* Furthermore, it provided the working classes with an opportunity to air their wit and sing *Where Did You Get That Hat?* thus taking their minds off their plight and stamping my name in the minds of promoters simultaneously.

"So this is Peter Pook, the schoolboy wonder, eh?" Tucker announced as I pushed his jersey off the only available peg. "First time you've worked for money they tell me, sonny. Does teacher know you're out late?"

I shrugged my shoulders modestly and looked the other way. "Go play with your coal-shovel, Tucker. Don't let's get familiar, please. It's bad enough having to thrash you as a stranger—don't make it harder for me."

"Oh, we got a right little shrinking violet here, mates. Too toffee-nosed to talk to his fellow-workers, eh?"

"I'd like to talk to you, Tucker, but I shall be using a lot of long words of two, even three syllables—so what's the point?"

"See that, mush? Do you know what that is?" Tucker held up a remarkably large fist, on which was tattooed *Life is rounded with a sleep.*

"Shakespeare, of course. From Prospero's speech in The Tempest."

"What in hell are you gabbling about? I means this dangerous object in front of your eyes."

"Oh, that thing. It's where normal people have a hand to show where their arm ends. It's like a foot but higher up. In your case, it's probably for lifting you off the canvas when the ref tells you it's safe to get up because you've lost. Don't worry about it—they'll give you a big glove to hide it in a minute. Look carefully and you'll find you've got another one to match on the left side."

"That's my home-made sleeping pill—for you, big mouth,

so watch your. . . ."

"Come on, you two. Take your partners for the next waltz," the promoter shouted through the door.

"You go out first, friend," I told my opponent politely, holding the door open for him. "Tradition decrees that the champion always enters the ring last."

Too thick to spot the innuendo, Tucker waddled out, followed by his manager, second and betting cronies. My sole supporter, Honners, was waiting for me in the aisle.

"Who is this hirsute bum?" Honners inquired in a loud voice when he saw Fireman Tucker, but the crowd began to sing *Where Did You Get That Hat?* so noisily that the remark was ignored.

"Didn't realize I was so popular in Southampton," I observed to Honners.

"Who is this hirsute bum?" Honners shouted, annoyed that no one heeded him. "I reckon they're rooting for Tucker. Make way for Peter Pook, the Cudford Infant, you provincial peasants —unless you want to get trodden underfoot."

Honners was causing quite a stir, not only for his size but also for the words enblazoned across his little jersey—the ancient Pilkington-Goldberg battle-cry, 'Come out and fight, you son-of-a-bitch'. A bystander wearing regulation evening dress of cap and collar-stud said, "He must be something to do with a circus—a flea-circus. Hallo, half-pint, hurry up and hop along to the ring."

The referee, balding Mr Ned Curtis of Winchester, greeted me sympathetically. "Take your funny hat off then, Pook. They tell me it's your first professional fight, so you won't have gone six rounds before."

"The most I've ever gone is three, so I don't intend staying longer tonight against fat boy here. Even three is boring— unless your programme is ahead of schedule and you want me to drag it out a bit."

"Thanks for the favour, Pook, but we're running right on time. Now, both of you, I want a clean sharp contest, with no mauling or dirty. . . ."

"Then let's wipe the vaseline off Tucker's pan for a start. He knows the rules as well as I do."

"Rule number one, Pook, is to shut up and allow me to handle the bout. How you can stand there like a male nude wearing that wet hat and criticising other people. . . ."

"And his shorts are too high—the waistband's practically under his armpits. He's supposed to wear shorts, not an off-the-shoulder blouse. He'll claim a foul every time he gets hit below that plunging neck-line."

"Maybe it's the way he's built."

"I've never heard of anybody built like a doughnut. He ought to be marked out like a tennis-court."

"You've got a mighty lot of lip for a beginner, Pook. This is going to be a properly governed contest under B.B.B. of C. rules. Now return to your corner and come out fighting at the bell—but for gawdsake take that stupid hat off first."

I did a little strut round the ring for the benefit of the press photographers, who clicked their cameras gratefully at something out of the ordinary at last. Seeing Curly Brown, of the *Cudford Echo,* I leaned over the ropes and called out, "Don't forget the big write-up, Curly boy—how about *The Fighting Toff* as a headline?"

"Sorry, Peter. The best I can do is a half-inch in column six of Minor Bouts."

"Half-inch! I'd get more than that as a lost poodle in the Classified Ads! Could you spare a whole inch if I put Tucker in your lap?"

The bell showed a complete contrast in styles, as the aggressive Tucker shuffled towards me rather like a cottage-loaf with arms. I danced around him on my toes, lightly jabbing the left to let the crowd see a classy performer in action before

Tucker went out. I noted with satisfaction a pimple on the right side of his face, marking the exact spot where shortly he was going to wonder if his jaw had been broken. If Tucker represented the new material of the craft, no wonder people were saying that boxing was on its way out.

"Try to loosen up and clump about the ring less awkwardly," I advised him. "Nothing irks me more than lack of style—you're spoiling the whole image of manly grace."

Suddenly Tucker became a flurry of thick arms and seemed to grow to a great height—all of eight feet tall. Just as I was trying to figure out this optical illusion I heard the referee counting, though for the life of me I couldn't remember hitting Tucker at that particular moment. Looking down, I was embarrassed to find myself on my knees, so I arose and laughed sportingly. "Guess I slipped, Tucker," I explained.

"Yus, you did, mate, and this is what you slipped on," he grunted, holding up his right mitt for my inspection. "I don't usually knock 'em down this early, but then you're new and don't know about us pro's."

"Would you two like a cup o' tea to chat over?" the referee inquired, dusting my gloves. "I only asked because it's the first time I've ever handled a pair of old maids. Cut the cackle and let's have some action."

The crowd howled delightedly at their hero's unexpected success, so I decided to end the exhibition of style and put Tucker to bed by round two with the heavy artillery. One's first job with a crude slugger is to cut him to pieces with dazzling attacks, especially to the body, until his sole aim in life is to get the referee between you and a concave belly. Once he is under the impression that a moped has rammed his stomach, it is a simple matter to put him out of his misery with a double on the unprotected jaw. I set about the task with my customary skill, a task made easier by Tucker's complete lack of defence. I wondered how such a crude performer could possibly be termed professional, because his only answer to my searing left was pathetic to watch, consisting of an uncoordinated flurry of gloves whirled over at random, in the hope that the law of averages might land one hit among so many shots.

"'You might just as well box with your eyes shut, windmilling like that," I told him derisively as I regained my feet after the law of averages had operated in his favour at last. "If you hope to scratch a living out of the fight game, I should make sure you've got a private income on the side so you can eat."

"Knocked you off your feet though, didn't I, Pook? Twice in one round ain't bad for a bloke what's only just beginning to warm up. I got the distance now, so wave good-bye to that toffee-nosed dwarf in your corner because they wants the ring soon for the main bout."

"Silence, both of you," Mr Curtis ordered sharply. "You been yapping away like you're interviewing each other on the radio."

"Well, ref, warn Tucker to stop boring in with his crewcut. I'm a boxer, not a barber. If he's exhausted, let him lie on the deck, not on me."

"Don't try to tell me how to conduct this shambles, Pook. You're paid to entertain the mob, not hold a fireside chat with Tucker."

"Who's a toffee-nosed dwarf?" demanded a shrill voice at my side angrily. It was Honners, whose brief appearance in the ring was terminated abruptly by being carried bodily out of it by Mr Curtis.

"What's this supposed to be—a fight or a family reunion?" Mr Curtis shouted vehemently. "No wonder you're getting the slow hand-clap from the mob."

"They're fed up with Tucker's stalling tactics. . . ."

"Shut up, Pook! You hold a debate on every single thing that happens in the blasted place. Give me some action or I'll disqualify the pair of you."

"It's too late now—there's the bell for the end of round one. Off I go to my corner to freshen up for round two."

I returned to my stool for the customary towel-waving, only to find Honners missing. He was over in Tucker's corner, still furious about being called a toffee-nosed dwarf, so I hurried across the ring to bring him back. This was easier said than done, and Mr Curtis joined us to see why all the participants were now in one corner of the ring, as though boxing had suddenly become a closed shop profession. Six of us coaxed Honners back to his own corner, a task made more difficult because he was suspended upside-down and bawling something about social justice for high-born shrimps.

"I've got a feeling I'm not managing the next world champion," Honners muttered disgruntledly, as he flapped the towel over me. "Another round like the first one and we'll have to bury you at sea."

"You just don't understand the professional fight scene, Honners. To go any place today you have to give the public what they want—blood and drama. Hence I string Tucker along, making him look good—with me as the gallant novice, all heart and guts but completely outclassed. They love that because that's the story of their own lives and they can identify themselves with me without getting hurt. Before you know where you are, the mob, with that characteristic sense of fair play so typical of the British, have changed sides completely and are screaming for Tucker's blood. 'Kill the fat useless bully,' they roar, 'Go get him, Pook, and break every bone in his ugly great body.' That's my cue for the big act. Apparently drawing on some hidden reserve of courage beyond the limit of human endurance, I fight back desperately and win. Knight in shining armour triumphs—exit dragon. Result, nobbins pour into ring, mob goes home happy, promoter signs me up for next bill as Your Favourite and My Favourite, That Crowd-pleasing

Toff in the Straw Boater—Peter Pook with the lethal hook."

Honners looked worried. "But does Tucker know the routine? If he does, all I can say is that he's overplaying his part."

"Of course Tucker doesn't know the routine. He's merely the clumsy stooge I toy with for effect. He's the unwitting straight man, or fall guy, as the Americans call it."

"How can he be the fall guy when it's you who's hit the deck twice?"

"Figures of speech, Honners. Admittedly he's had a couple of lucky breaks but from now on I operate to plan by setting up the situation for maximum dramatic impact and sensational audience-reaction. I'm an artist, Honners, not a run-of-the-mill slugger like Tucker. Finesse will always beat a brawler."

"I hope you're right, Peter. At the moment it's hard to see you as the obvious victor. You remind me for all the world of an artist who's winning the hard way. Perhaps your mettle is being hardened in the forge of defeat, and all that gum they preach when you're being beaten to pulp."

Mr Curtis called from the centre of the ring, "The bell's gone, Pook. . . ."

"I'm not surprised, with a thieving mob like this around. They'll have the stopwatch next. Let's hope you locked the changing-room door. . . ."

"I mean the bell's gone for the second round—so perhaps the House would adjourn the debate so you can spare the time to take part in the proceedings of the night. Tucker can hardly box on his own."

"Tucker can hardly box whichever way you look at it."

"Listen to me, Pook; get in there and produce some kind of an exhibition, understand? You've given us nothing but jaw ever since you entered the ring."

Mr Curtis waved us to continue with an impatient gesture, whereupon I darted round the ring, flashing lefts to the target till Tucker blinked bewilderedly. In desperation he made a defensive wall of gloves and forearms, bending almost double to escape the storm. Just as I had him going, he straightened up suddenly, catching my chin with his bullet head.

"Foul, ref!" I shouted indignantly.

"It certainly was," Mr Curtis agreed. "At least you're honest about it, Pook, so don't do it again and I won't penalize you this time. My job would sure be a lot easier if more pugs would own up like you did."

"Own up? I'm complaining, not owning up! It was a deliberate foul."

"Spoken like a man, Pook. Don't do it again, that's all."

"Do what again?"

"Rabbit-punch a man when he's crouching, of course. Box on."

"But Tucker used his head!"

"All good fighters use their heads. Sporting of you to praise your opponent like that."

"You mean I ought to use my head too?"

"Of course. That's what distinguishes the champion from the crude slugger. Now box on in silence."

Well, that's professional boxing, I told myself philo-sophically. I caught on quickly to the new tactics, and directly an opening presented itself I let Tucker have it on the jaw with my own head. Tucker screamed "Foul" as though he was being throttled with my bare hands, and Mr Curtis intervened to give me a public warning.

"A deliberate and disgraceful foul," he told me angrily.

I stared at him bewildered. "I used my head," I protested.

"Exactly. Can't understand you, Pook. Every time you do something wrong you stop to confess. That's no excuse—you simply mustn't do it in the first place. I realize this is your first professional contest but surely you know that under no circumstances are you allowed to use your head."

"All I can say is you must be going off yours."

"Box on before I disqualify you, Pook. At this rate I wouldn't put it past you to kick Tucker."

"If I do I'll own up first, in case you're his manager on the side."

My equanimity unruffled by this strange interpretation of the rules, I continued to treat the spectators to a display of the finer arts of ring-craft right through round two, dazzling Tucker with my footwork as I showed him how a master can box just as effectively on the retreat. The sporting British crowd soon took me to their hearts by booing and throwing two beer bottles into the ring, then inquiring as to the chances of a four-minute mile. Stung to fury, I let Tucker have the left hook to the head, so that he sagged against the ropes. Immediately I gave him the finisher in the same fashion, but he dropped on one knee when he saw it, with the result that my flashing hook went over his head and caught Mr Curtis on the jaw. The referee went down too, and the crowd chanted delightedly "Ring-a-ring-of-roses, all fall down!"

Worriedly I began to help Mr Curtis to his feet, only to be knocked down by Tucker. My opponent's triumph was short-lived, because he joined me on the canvas, felled from behind by a stool wielded by Honners.

When order was finally restored in the hall and Mr Curtis had recovered from the accident, he called us to the centre of the ring and addressed us grimly. "All right, men, so we'll call the whole thing an act of God, like earthquakes. Pook slugged me by accident; Tucker hit Pook to protect me, Honners coshed Tucker to protect Pook; Tucker's second kicked Honners out of the ring to protect someone else; Honners hit a steward for a reason not yet established—and so it goes on. Now, seeing we've only hired the hall for five hours and the main bout's due on at nine o'clock, and remembering that people have paid to see a fight rather than a play, we'll just skip the court of inquiry and do four more rounds, understand?

"But Tucker hit me when the contest was temporarily stopped," I reminded him, "therefore you have no option but to disqualify him and give me the decision."

"I'll tell you one thing, Pook—if anyone's going to be disqualified it's you. Box on."

"That mouthy little elf you carries with you for luck bashed my 'ead with a stool," Tucker grumbled, rubbing his dandruff.

"Can you sing as well as act?" I inquired.

"Silence, the pair of you. Any more lip and I'll declare no contest—that means neither of you gets paid."

Immediately the ring became a flurry of blows and slaps as we leapt into action simultaneously, flailing away at each other at close quarters until Tucker had to spoil such spirited action by losing his right glove.

"Your glove fell off—bad lacing," I explained, stepping back sportingly in case it was a trick.

Mr Curtis picked it up. "Of course his glove came off with you holding it tight under your armpit, Pook. Don't hold, understand. Box on."

With such a biassed referee I decided to go for the quick knock-out by employing the first trick my old grandfather taught me—the eyes right. I waited till I caught Tucker's eyes staring into mine during round three, then looked deliberately away to the right, simultaneously letting him have the left hook on his blind side. This sharp manoeuvre worked with practised precision, although I was surprised to find myself sitting on the stool in my corner. I said to Honners, "Is the fight over then?" and Honners replied, "Not if you can come out for round four?"

"Is Tucker still on his feet then?"

"No, he's sitting over there in his own corner."

"Has he had enough then?"

"No, but he reckons you have. What made you look out of the ring so he could sock you on the chin? Luckily the bell saved you. Do you feel game for another round?"

"Didn't he go down then?"

"No, but you did. They gave you a count of eight, then the bell went for the end of the round. Here's Curtis to see how you are."

I looked at Mr Curtis with a confident grin. "Hallo, Vicar. Plenty more up my sleeve," I said cheerily, to let him see I was in peak condition.

"You sure you're all right, Pook?"

"Fit as sin. Everything's going to a carefully laid plan."

"You mean you even plan how to lose?"

"Showmanship, Mr Curtis. Give the fans their money's worth and they'll come again."

"Very well then, I'll see how you shape this round."

"Could I have an extra minute to confer with my second?"

"No."

Honners was rubbing my legs energetically. "Now see if you can stand up, Peter," he ordered. I stood up and sat down again rather quickly.

"Funny. I'm strong as an ox up top but the pins are a bit wobbly."

"That's nothing to worry about, Peter. Get Tucker in a clinch and hold on like mad this round while you recover. Then freeze him in the last round."

"Let's get through this round before we worry about that."

"Look, Peter, I'll put my arm round your waist and come with you as far as the centre of the ring. Then grab him." My legs were still shaky from the knock-down but Honners helped me to the centre for round four. Mr Curtis stared at us unbelievingly. "This isn't like cricket, where you can have a runner if you're injured," he told us.

"It's only my legs, Mr Curtis. If Honners walks me about a bit they'll start working again."

"Are you suggesting that Honners holds you up while you

fight Tucker? Get out of the ring immediately, Honners. Box on or I'll stop the fight."

As you will recall, I was always most dangerous when in trouble, as Tucker was soon to discover. Directly he led with a left I stepped under it and fell on him, supporting myself round his ample stomach. Tucker backed away, dragging me with him as though he was saving me at sea, until the crowd began to sing *The Anniversary Waltz*. Mr Curtis forced his way between to separate us, only to find that now he was firmly attached to me instead. "Let go of me this instant, Pook," he ordered, perturbed to hear spectators inquiring if the excuse-me dance was open to anybody.

I released Mr Curtis and was surprised to find myself sitting on a stool which Honners pushed under me from the ringside. I sat there weary but grateful while Mr Curtis tried to take in the new situation. "What the devil do you think you're doing, sitting down in the middle of a round?" he demanded at last.

Honners interrupted. "I expect you are going to warn Pook for holding, Mr Curtis."

"I certainly am—but what's that to do with it?"

"Only that there's nothing in the rules to say a man can't sit down while he's being warned."

"Have you gone off your tiny rocker, man? A boxer sit down during a contest?—no one ever even considered it, let alone put it in the rule book. You'll stop the bout so he can have his dinner next."

"With great respect, Mr Curtis, I've got the book here and there's nothing to say he can't have his dinner."

"Why, you stupid little twit, there's nothing in the book to say he mustn't get married between rounds, because. . . ."

Honners quickly climbed into the ring with the rule book, thumbing the index under M for Marriage during rounds, at the same time thrusting it under the referee's nose. While doing so, he darted a glance at me, then at my legs until I got the message. By the time everybody was satisfied that there was no rule against a boxer conducting a public auction or enlisting in His Majesty's Armed Forces during a contest, I had fully recovered from the effects of round three and no longer required the stool. In fact, I was even able to clench my fists once more and raise my arms.

Confidence rapidly returned to me, enabling me to concentrate on the task of proving that a good boxer will always beat a brawler. Admittedly this art had to be practised on the retreat, by running backwards round the ring to avoid Tucker's crude attempts to get near me.

"How many laps will you do before the fight starts?" Mr Curtis demanded, as he pivoted in the centre of the canvas to follow the chase.

"Tactics," I gasped. "I'm wearing down his legs for the last round. Why worry?—the crowd's excited."

They were indeed, standing up and howling for Tucker to stay put and wait for me to come round to him. "Armchair critics—they figure I'm losing," I added. "They react to drama but don't understand it."

"What they don't understand is how you're still on your feet. Why don't you stop back-pedalling and have a last desperate fling with Tucker for a change? That ought to be dramatic enough for them."

This was exactly what I had in mind, because, without warning, I suddenly came forward and met Tucker with a flurry of well-timed blows. Surprised and panting, he stood there looking a sorry picture. His jaw sagged as he tried to catch his breath.

"That took the steam out of you, eh, Tucker?" I jeered. "Thought I was finished, didn't you? Teach you to train properly next time you fight. You're all wind and fat."

"Silence, Pook," Mr Curtis interrupted. "Save your breath for later and listen to the count. . . . Three . . . four . . . five . . . six. . . . "

I got up at nine, then made sure Mr Curtis wiped my gloves clean. "I'm only supposed to ensure there's no dirt on them, Pook, not clean and polish them like shoes. Box on."

But it had been long enough to get me to the bell for the end of the round and one whole minute of blissful rest. I lay in Honners' arms with my eyes shut, like The Death of Nelson.

"Don't forget the plan in the next round," Honners bawled into my ear.

"Shut up and go to sleep. We'll talk about it in the morning."

"You're not in bed, Peter. If you don't wake up I'll have to throw the towel in."

"Good idea. While you're at it, throw me in with it."

"Oh, so you want to quit, eh? All right, Peter, leave it to me. You go to sleep and don't worry any more."

Then I experienced a violent awakening as the thin nozzle of a sal volatile bottle was thrust up my nostril and a sharp instrument like a pin entered my right buttock. Opening my eyes in pain, I discovered Honners pulling me to my feet by my ear. Into the other ear he was screaming "Get out there and fight, you useless oaf, or I'll cut your throat with a rusty nail."

I learned afterwards that Honners had a small side bet on the contest, but at the moment I was being propelled towards the centre of the ring by means of Honners' head in the small of my back.

"Is he all right for the next round?" Mr Curtis inquired.

"Merely foxing, Mr Curtis. Don't let him fool you—he's specially trained for an all-action finale."

"He don't look like it at the moment, unless he's been trained for a chess tournament. Maybe it's the lull before the calm."

Honners lifted up my hands to boxing pose, saying, "Come on, Peter lad, get weaving like we planned. Come on, boy, fight," as though addressing a reluctant race-horse. Then, by holding my elbows, thrust my fists in the general direction of Tucker.

"This is ridiculous," Mr Curtis snapped impatiently. "I can't have three of you in the ring playing puppets. I'll have no option but to award the bout to Tucker."

"Then let me fight Tucker instead," Honners suggested, but Tucker was in no mood for further delay. Brushing Honners aside he barked, "That's who I signed to fight and I'm having him while he's cold." Whereupon he threw a series of punches in my direction which I easily warded off with my face. But Tucker's arrogant manner stung me to a new fury, especially as I had noticed that his right eye was completely closed. Shut the other one, I figured, and I could still pull the fight out of the fire.

Remembering the second trick my grandfather taught me, I told Tucker "Listen, Nelson, your right eye's closed, so watch while I bung up the other one for you." Simultaneously I walloped him good and hard in the stomach with devastating effect. In the clinch that followed I said "So you can't take it in the belly, eh? Well that's where you're going to get the next one." While he was thinking about this I clouted him on the jaw with all I had left. Tucker staggered backwards on the ropes, then disappeared as if by magic. Then I caught a glimpse of his boots sticking out of the Press row at the ringside and Curly Brown, the *Echo* reporter, lying on the ground. Also in the melée was Honners, his shrill voice screaming "Start the count, ref, while I help him up! Take your dirty hands off me, you overgrown ape, and help Tucker beat the count!"

The latter remark seemed to be addressed to a steward who was apparently bent on arresting Honners for pulling the rope down when Tucker fell against it, thus leaving the ring for lack of the customary support. It was difficult to see how Honners was assisting Tucker to beat the count because both Honners and Tucker suddenly fell over the back of the Press row into row two, as though his aim was to roll my opponent out of the building the hard way. Even the steward was now in danger of being somersaulted into row three, until the spectators took a hand and threw Honners across the aisle into the five-and-nines. The steward was upside-down in row three but of Tucker there was no sign. Eventually he was located under the seats of row two, none the worse for the experience except for unexplained teeth marks in his thigh.

Meanwhile, Mr Curtis had no alternative but to award the decision to me, although the stewards pointed out that this was to come under review when an inquiry into the whole matter was held. Any such inquiry would necessitate the presence of Honners as a key witness—or defendant, as one steward referred to him—but at the moment Honners was conspicuous by his absence. He certainly wasn't in the five-and-nines or anywhere else, so I quickly changed my clothes and hoped to meet him on the last train from Southampton Central to Cudford. Worse still, the promoter, Dave Wilkins refused to give me the prize-money, stating that if the inquiry found in my favour he would post it to me, but on no account did he ever want to see me again, win or lose. I tried poverty, then tears and a broken heart but he was adamant, so I threatened to beat him up in his office, until five of his boys came in so I left quietly.

Outside the hall there was a small demonstration in the form of a picket. I read the banners they were carrying, all condemning boxing as a brutal and barbarous sport which should be banned. Others demanded government action to make it illegal in this country. Some of the demonstrators were handing leaflets to passers-by, while a girl was asking them to sign a petition. A small boy gave me a leaflet and said to me, "Read this, sir, then go over and sign the petition to have this cruel

126

sport outlawed. In your case you might even join us."

Recognizing the voice, I looked more closely at the boy in the dark and discovered it was Honners. "You could be right, chum," I told him. "Give me the pen."

Honners grinned up at me. "Then let's get out of here fast." he chuckled.

EIGHT

After the fight fiasco it was Honners who thought up an easier way for us to make money. He approached the subject by the analytical method, thus: "Ordinary men have nothing to offer the world but a pair of hands and two flat feet, Peter, but we possess personality, immense social charm, and—in my case— brains. Therefore let's cash in on our patent advantages over the mob and clean up during the summer vacation."

"How do you mean exactly, little friend?"

"I've spotted an ad in your magazine *Brute Strength,* seeking personable young men of integrity to act as social escorts for lonely ladies in the big city. Obviously beamed at you and me. Just imagine it, Peter, you get a good night out at the pictures, with a Chinese and beer afterwards—and the doll pays! It's nature's answer to sex."

"Who's making this fantastic offer on behalf of all men?— a male suffragette?"

"Read it yourself, Peter, in Miscellaneous, just under that one for *au pair* girls. 'The London Rent-a-Gent Bureau requires personable young men-about-town to escort lady visitors to our shores for all social occasions. Ability to dance essential. We pay top rates for the right dates' and so on."

I took the magazine from Honners and checked for myself, wondering why such joyful tidings were hidden away on page 18 instead of being headlined on the front page. "Now I know what the old saying means about the woman always pays," I sighed happily. "Throw everything overboard for the time being and let's sign on as soon as possible."

Exactly one week later, Honners and I walked rapidly down Regent Street in our desperate search for easy money, towards that part of London where one finds some of the cleverest and most ruthless business men in Europe, little suspecting that some years hence I should be plodding these very streets as an author visiting his Publishers, with the same objective. However, on this fine day in the summer vacation such formidable undertakings were far from my mind as we searched for the luxurious offices of the London Rent-a-Gent Bureau so impressively illustrated in the magazine ad—where handsome dinner-jacketed men strode in one palatial suite, then emerged laughingly from another, arm-in-arm with gorgeous model girls whom they handed in to a convoy of Rolls parked along the fashionable boulevard. In particular, I liked the manner in which the bronzed young men debonairly waved to friends with their gloves and laughed gaily to bystanders as they directed the chauffeurs towards the delights of the West End.

Now it seemed that the offices of the London Rent-a-Gent Bureau in narrow little Curly Street did not fill the entire building as had been depicted in the ad. Instead, they were situated on the top floor of a tall edifice which reminded me of a converted warehouse. Just inside the entrance lobby was a names-board informing the public that a general cross-section of Britain's commercial life was packed into its six storeys on the sardine principle, from Potato Factors (Export) to Contraceptive Supplies Ltd. (Wholesale Only). Midway between these enterprises was a Madam Mifser (Crystal Ball, Stars and Palms) and a certain Professor Malvani who followed a strange calling listed as Hair Removed By Appointment Only; Moles and Warts Thursday; Ear Piercing Friday; Closed Saturday All Day.

"I wonder what he does Sunday—circumcisions?" Honners remarked as we made our way up to floor six, listed as the London Rent-a-Gent Social Bureau; Male Escorts for all occasions; Tails Extra; Day and Night Rent-a-Gent Facilities; Dance Partners and Best Men at Short Notice; Waiters, Footmen, Butlers, Party Guests, Mourners available; Models, Godfathers, M.C.s, Couriers, Hosts, Chairmen, Ushers, Toastmasters, Croupiers, Well-Wishers, Handbill Distributors arranged.

"What do you want to be, Peter?" Honners asked on the way up. "A Mourner or a Handbill Distributor?"

"As far as I'm concerned I'm all for Rent-a-Gent. For my money they can call themselves Hire-a-Sire."

"Surely you wouldn't go that far?"

"Just tempt me with the right cash inducement."

We discovered that the top floor was not wholly occupied by London's greatest social bureau, being shared with French Lessons Any Hour of the Day or Night; Rare Fish Bought, Sold and Stuffed; Exotic Pictures & Continental Books; and Artificial Eyeballs, Every Socket Size in Stock. The London Rent-a-Gent Bureau sprawled over two small rooms, one of which was apparently sublet to Why Be Bald Ltd., so we knocked at the correct door and squeezed inside. Mr Zackerman, the Principal, sat at his desk in a room so small that his secretary used one end of the desk for her typewriter. On Mr Zackerman's instructions Honners closed the door so I could sit at the same desk on the visitor's chair, then Honners had to stand as best he could between Mr Zackerman and the secretary. Mr Zackerman apologized profusely for the lack of space. "Sorry for the squeeze, gentlemen, but you know what it is in London these days. As a special favour to an old friend I've had to sub-let our outer office to Why Be Bald Ltd. It sounds ridiculous, but I'll have to ask Mr Honners here to kneel on the floor a second while I open the filing-cabinet and take out the relevant file. Thank you—just a trifle lower, please; it's in the middle drawer. Ah, that's it, thank you. You could sit on the desk if you don't mind holding the phone on your lap. Excuse my knees, Mr Pook, but come tight up to the desk so that Barbara can put the typewriter on the landing while you're here. I didn't bargain for both of you coming in together."

"Had we known you were so short of space I'd have worn a thinner suit," Honners told him coldly. If this is London's greatest social bureau as the advertisement stated, I asked myself puzzledly, what can the lesser ones be like? I imagined they must operate from headquarters situated in large cupboards. My train of thought was interrupted when the office door half opened, to thrust me hard against the desk, and a bald-headed man exposed as much of his body diagonally as was possible under the circumstances. "Hallo, Reuby," Mr Zackerman greeted the newcomer. "Sorry you can't get in but, as you can see, it's our busy day at the moment. What can I do for you?"

"I was wondering if it would be convenient to borrow Barbara just now, to do the letters. Solly's gone out, so there's room enough for the next hour."

"Sure thing, Reuby. You take Barbara, then Mr Honners here can sit down. The typewriter's on the landing anyway. Perhaps Mr Pook will be so kind as to stand up so we can get Barbara out, then we'll all be as cosy as sin." When Reuby and Barbara had departed Mr Zackerman explained that, owing to the acute shortage of staff in London, he shared his secretary with Why Be Bald Ltd., the latter enjoying her services every afternoon when Solly went out, apparently to make room for her. "Does Solly own Why Be Bald Ltd?" Honners inquired.

"Oh no, Reuby is Why Be Bald Ltd. Solly shares his office for Don't Be Fat & Co."

"I bet if Solly was fat he couldn't share the office, eh?"

"That's the odd thing about it—Solly's fat as a pig. That's why he has to go out every afternoon to try and get his weight down."

"Then if Reuby is Why Be Bald Ltd. why has he got a head like a peeled apple? Surely if bald people see Reuby and fat people see Solly it's enough to put them out of business."

"Ah, that's the point, they don't see them. Treatment by post only—positively no callers. If you check on Reuby's ads in the Classifieds you'll find a picture of Reuby looking like his glands have gone wrong and produced a stook of Canadian wheat on his head. He only uses his normal photo to show what it was like before he rubbed in Instant Sprouto or whatever he calls the muck. Between you and me, I've known Reuby for years and I'm positive it's been the stuff itself that's sent him bald as a greengage. Not that he's not sincere, mind. As he says in the ads, he believes in the product so firmly that he's used it himself for years. What he doesn't state is what it's done to his scalp. Same with Solly. Solly has to use a model in his ads who looks like he's on holiday from Belsen. Solly told me only last week he's been obliged to abandon the Don't Be Fat course because it doesn't suit him—he's out of his suit already, and can't hardly get up these stairs no more. I told him it would be a nice thing, fatso's ringing up from all over the country for advice, and me having to tell them the boss ain't in to answer because he's too bloomin' bloated to climb the stairs to his own office. He's already thinking of changing over to a new line, Don't Be Thin & Co. The way he's going, he'll have to call it Don't Be Fat—Be Enormous."

"What about that beautiful secretary of yours—does she need an escort?" I asked hopefully, to bring the conversation back to our visit.

"Only when you're around, by the looks of things. Barbara's my personal secretary and strictly out of bounds. Now, boys, let's get down to business. Tell me, Peter, why have you brought your son to a place like this?"

"My son! That's Honners, a good friend of mine."

"Oh, I see. Afraid there's little call for midgets in this game. I suppose he could be a handbill distributor though—he's the right height for letter-boxes."

Honners flushed red with indignation. "Listen to me, Zackerman," he piped viciously. "Discerning people appreciate I'm a pearl among pumpkins, if you get the analogy. I ooze charm like a slashed rubber tree because I'm a pedigree nob of the blood. Peter may be more of a sexy giraffe, but I specialize in cultural chat and upper-class wit. Note the finely chiselled clock, perfect except for a slight elevation of the beak in the classic coat-hook mould of aristocracy. Consequently I am bred to mix suavely with all classes—even yours, if you will permit the slur. What woman wouldn't give her all for such a companion?"

Mr Zackerman shrugged his shoulders. "All right then, I'll take a chance, seeing we're short-handed this week. Are you free this evening?"

"No, I'm not free this evening or any other time. You can pay me the standard Rent-a-Gent scale or I quit. I'm in this racket for money—not experience."

"No, I mean can you start work right away?"

"You name it and we'll escort it."

"Good for you, Honners. Oh, excuse me one second while I answer the phone. Hallo—oh, yes, this is Professor Dagostini speaking; what is your problem this time, Mr Robinson. Oh, I see. I'm afraid complete rest of the larynx is the only solution. Yes. Gargling helps, of course, but on no account must you attempt lesson six while your voice is in that condition. I can hardly hear you on the phone as it is. Yes, I realize lesson five contains some extremely high notes . . . no, please don't attempt them over the phone . . . oh my gawd! . . . No more just now, please, Mr Robinson—you could seriously injure your windpipe. Rest up for at least two weeks. . . . Of course I understand. . . . I shall instruct our musical director at once to withhold lesson seven until we hear from you that all is well . . . entirely at our expense, naturally. Spend the time revising Theory and learning the words of Granada—but under no circumstances are you to attempt singing it, especially over the phone to me. No, no, Mr Robinson, rest assured that this understandable setback will in no way affect the award of your College Diploma in Music. When we guarantee success or your fees refunded, we mean just that or we should not have enrolled you in the first place—anyone with a voice like yours deserves a Diploma as fast as we can present it. Good. Now don't forget what I said about complete rest for the voice— don't even phone me for three weeks. The entire tutorial staff and student body of You Too Can Sing Academy send you their heartfelt good wishes for a speedy recovery from lesson five."

Mr Zackerman replaced the phone and wiped his brow. "That Robinson fellow will drive me off my rocker before he's finished the course, gentlemen. Personal tuition by post surely doesn't mean singing me each lesson over the phone to see if he's got the hang of it. Last week he gave me *In a Monastery Garden* right through. He made it sound more like *In a Public House* on New Year's Eve."

"But what's all this got to do with the escort business? I inquired puzzledly. "Surely we don't have to sing to the girls as well?"

"Oh, of course not, Peter. I forgot to explain. Among my various enterprises I represent You Too Can Sing Academy.

Our ad always depicts a young man singing at Covent Garden, with the caption; He Got Here By Mail—You Too Can Sing Through The Post."

"Where is this academy then?"

"Right here in this office, Peter. I do the lot, if you will permit me to say so. Now to business. Ah, yes, I knew it was in this file. Two young ladies want to do the town tonight, expense no object. They've just flown in from British Columbia —no, I tell a lie—from Boston. Anyhow, what's the difference —it's a hell of a long way however you look at it. Meet at eight. You receive a flat rate of a guinea each, but give the girls a high time and who knows!—most of my clients are lavish tippers. Any points to iron out before your first assignment?"

"Do we meet here and pick up the Rolls outside?" Honners asked, remembering the advertisement.

"This is a classy trade, Honners, so don't mention Rolls.

You'll be taking them round the corner for a fish-and-chip supper in newspaper next. You'll probably be eating at the Café Royal, boy."

"I mean the Rolls-Royce and chauffeur, like we saw in your ad."

"Oh, I follow you. Sorry, but all the Rolls are booked tonight. Hail a cab and charge it to us, though I must admit that some of our escorts make a bit on the side by taking the bus. Feel out the girls first—they may prefer to walk and see London by night. The radio says no rain, so it's an idea worth considering. Give them the old chat about local atmosphere and seeing the peasants at first-hand, rather than missing the bustle and smell in a cab. Pick them up at the Giovani Commercial Hotel, Tipher Street, eight sharp. All the details are here in this form. The rest is up to you, so the best of luck."

Sauntering along Curly Street and studying the form, Honners and I learned that the two girls whom we were to escort that evening were Gaynor and Carmen Laskanski. There was little else we could discover from the particulars because they consisted mainly of copious references and cross-references peculiar to the Rent-a-Gent filing system, such as code numbers and little boxes containing ticks to indicate that from now on the two girls would never escape the clutches of Mr Zackerman's follow-up brochures.

"Must be sisters, by the sound of it," Honners commented. "Let's toss up to see who escorts who."

"Too risky, Honners. Wait till we meet them, then you take the short one and I'll have the long job. Girls always come in two sizes—look at Brandy and Olga."

We presented ourselves at eight o'clock in the foyer of the hotel for the pick up, dressed in the heavy fashion of the day to make our seventeen years look more like fifty. Honners had carefully brushed talc powder into his hair as though he was going grey with age, while I had lightly rubbed mascara under my eyes, to simulate the bags of dissipation. Both of us walked slightly bent under the weight of many winters, although I had previously scotched Honners' idea of shuffling into the hotel with the aid of sticks. At the approach of two females we raised our black Homburg hats, causing a slight fall of talc powder to Honners' shoulders like dandruff.

"Hallo, boys," the stout short lady said jovially. "Have you seen two men come in while you've been waiting here?"

Honners screwed up his face to look wrinkled. "No, mam, but my friend and I are here to meet two ladies from Boston."

"Why, Carmen and I are from Boston. Have you brought a message from our escorts then?"

"We are your escorts, mam," Honners replied miserably, eyeing the tall girl and sizing up the situation. "But you're only kids! I'm old enough to be your mother— in fact I *am* Carmen's mother. How old are you, sonny?"

"Afraid I'm the wrong side of thirty," Honners said vaguely, "but life has been very worrying, especially since I lost my family."

"Lost your family! I should think your family lost you! Were you born grey or did the tragedy of going to school turn your hair white?"

Rather than prolong Honners' embarrassment I stepped in to do the introductions, explaining that, owing to the demand for escorts at this time of year, I had been forced to secure the services of child labour in the shape of Honners. "I'm his uncle," I added, to preserve the proprieties. "Now that we know each other, where would you ladies like to go?"

Gaynor looked at Honners with amusement. "Well, if it was Christmas, I'd like to take him to the pantomime." Honners could contain his wrath no longer. "Don't you dare mother me, mam. I'll have you understand I am a sophisticated, widely-travelled man of the world, not to mention a family tree with half the Tate Gallery up it. Furthermore, I have visited the

States and mixed with the top Boston froth, in which the name of Laskanski was conspicuous by its absence."

"Heavens above, love, we've never even been to the States. My daughter and I are merely down from Boston in Lincolnshire for some shopping and a run around the town. This is our third trip since my husband passed away."

"One can only congratulate him on making such an understandable decision, madam," Honners retorted rudely. "And for your information, ladies, the elongated toad with the black eyes is not my uncle but an ex-friend whom I, in a misplaced fit of philanthropy, tried to raise to his present social strata—in short, ladies, the gutter." Gaynor and Carmen laughed so much that tears blurred their eyes.

"What a delightful little character you are, to be sure," Gaynor cried. "Certainly the best we've ever had from Rent-a-Gent. What a marvellous evening there is ahead of us after all."

"His ex-friends often refer to him as Sir Short-arse the Bold," I threw in to stabilize the situation.

"I can be highly comical," Honners hissed icily, "but at the moment I am being bitter and devastatingly sardonic."

"And you do both most beautifully, Honners," Gaynor cut in. Whereupon she linked her arm through his, jerking the little fellow off his feet and through the revolving doors, crying, "Here we come, London, for the evening of our lives!"

While Honners stamped up and down the pavement, working off his temper by screaming and swearing for a taxi, I got to know Carmen quicker than most. She had the habit of taking one's arm and momentarily nestling her head on one's shoulder as though we were childhood sweethearts reunited. "I'm nineteen," she confided, "at least, I shall be tomorrow."

"Not all that younger than me, dear, so many happy returns of the day." With that, I kissed her, thinking to myself what an ideal way to make a living and wondering how Dr Windebank would record my career as a gigolo on the school's Valedictory Roll.

Honners had not so much secured a cab in the meantime as got himself involved in a verbal dispute with a taxi-driver, who had pulled into the kerb to find out why a total stranger should call him a peak-capped gorilla in a mobile cage. "I've flattened mouthy little squirts like 'im for less than that," the cabbie fumed, as Gaynor tried to pacify him by a combination of charm and double tipping. Even a London cabdriver is not immune to financial inducement, grudgingly allowing us to enter his vehicle on condition that there was no more lip from Snow White, as he put it. "All safely aboard me mobile cage then?" he inquired pointedly.

Honners mumbled something about poking the fare between the bars, but I silenced him tactfully by a hand across his mouth, while Gaynor asked the driver to take us to the Empire Palace.

"I happen to be *persona grata* at all the great London residences," Honners threw off airily, "but this one escapes my mind, unless it is the new town house of the Duke of Belter."

"It's a music-hall, Honners," Gaynor explained. "Nothing like a variety show to start off a good evening. Puts you in the mood for better things to come."

"Well, you can't start much lower, that's all I can say. Heaven forbid that any of my friends should see me there or that news of such a sordid venture should reach the ears of *The Tatler.* It's like when Dorian Gray slid off into the night to the junkies in Limehouse."

Perhaps Fate heard Honners' remark and arranged for the spotlight to pick out his little grey head in the stalls, when Rajah Must called for a volunteer from the audience. Never one to keep his nose out of anything, Honners climbed on the stage of the Empire Palace towards the end of the second half of the show and beamed happily at the packed auditorium, bowing easily to the applause as though mounting the steps was a difficult trick. He still held the hand of the shapely maiden in tights who had led him up, then kissed it with a courtly bow.

"Ah, welcome, welcome, little chota sahib—it is the honour of my life to greet you," Rajah Must boomed, in the extravagant patter of the theatre. "How brave in one of your age to assist me in my most magnificent illusion—although I am not certain whether you are very young or extremely old. Now, my worthy friend, let me make you taller, eh? That you would like, eh?"

Honners smirked superiorly at such attention. "It is well said that we cannot gild the lily; nevertheless, I offer my body up freely for such an experiment. The girl led Honners to the magic table in the centre of the stage, where she helped him lie down in a kind of multi-coloured coffin, too short even for Honners. She closed the lid, leaving his head and feet protruding at each end, then kissed his brow tenderly as though his last hour approached. From our seats we could clearly hear Honners asking her if she possessed a cosy coffin for two, but she merely smiled and withdrew. Rajah Must entered with a great show of mystery, muttered a suitable eastern spell over the audience and Honners, then, as the lights dimmed, rapidly thrust swords through the coffin at every angle.

"Mincemeat!" Honners gasped aloud. The audience were too enthralled to laugh, but, catching my eye, Honners winked, adding "Rent-a-Sieve".

"Now to lengthen our brave little talkative sahib," Rajah Must intoned, taking a timber saw and cutting through the centre of the coffin. To prove his action, he pulled Honners top half away and walked through the gap. The audience burst into surprised applause at the unexpectedness of the feat, even louder when Honners bowed his head in the horizontal position.

Rajah Must came forward to acknowledge the reception, holding up his beringed hands for silence. "Ladies and gentlemen, you may have seen a person sawn in half before, but the next illusion never! Watch closely, please."

Rajah Must carefully slid the coffin together once more until the two halves fitted. Then he gently pushed Honners' head inside at one end and the feet in the other. Over the coffin he draped a Union Jack flag just long enough for his incantation in Hindi, removing it with a dramatic sweep of his arm. We stared spellbound as Rajah Must opened the coffin—empty.

The illusionist strutted the stage to take his applause, bowing till the plume above his turban touched the footlights. "Have no fear, ladies and gentlemen. You have all heard of the celebrated Indian rope trick—now witness it before your very eyes."

So saying, Rajah Must took a coil of rope, which he threw upwards to the flies of the stage with a dexterous flick of his arm. The rope remained upright, stiff as a rod, and, still gazing steadfastly at the audience, Rajah Must commanded Honners to descend to earth, as he phrased it. Apparently Honners preferred to stay in Heaven, for there was no sign of him where the limelight indicated we might expect to see his feet appear. Rajah Must stared up to the flies and clapped his hands impatiently, while the orchestra gave a second roll of drums. Evidently there was a slight delay and we were playing for time.

"Do not be shy, little sahib; return from the spirit world and show thyself to us once more," Rajah Must bellowed upwards in a tone pitched to warn his contacts in the spirit world that further delay might well jeopardize their jobs in this world.

I distinctly heard a spirit voice from above inform the master that "he ain't up here, guvner," whereupon a bodiless head from the wings confirmed that Honners had not passed him during transmigration. Turning to the audience with outstretched arms, Rajah Must announced: "Ladies and gentlemen, such a unique and difficult illusion takes a little time, as you will understand. Please bear with me while I go into trance state and communicate with the spirit world of Lishti, that I may receive instruction through my guide, the Great Cabana."

Pausing only to close his eyes and place both hands on his forehead, Rajah Must fell into trance on the dot` then appeared to sleep-walk off the stage into the wings for a short séance with the Great Gabana. Meanwhile the orchestra allayed our fears by playing the lovely old ballad, *Will Ye Nae Come Back Again?*

I sensed that the delay was not just part of such a serious act, a feeling increased by what followed. I am in no way psychic myself, yet I experienced little difficulty in sharing with Rajah Must the message transmitted by the Great Gabana from the spirit world. First I heard Rajah Must's plea to his guide to "tell me where in hell the little twirp's gone or you're fired on the spot". I was staggered at the unorthodox reply from the other side: "I'm —— if I know, Charlie. One thing's for sure— 'e ain't up 'ere."

Rajah Must terminated the séance with the Hindustani valediction, "sodditt".

"That's a relief," I whispered to Gaynor. "The Great Gabana definitely states that Honners isn't up there in the spirit world."

Before Gaynor could reply, the theatre manager came to the footlights and folded his hands, as one about to impart bad news. "Ladies and gentlemen, I am sure you will understand that in such an elaborate illusion as you have witnessed, much complex apparatus is required, and at the moment I regret to inform you that the young gentleman who so sadly volunteered to assist Rajah Must has temporarily disappeared. . . ."

"That's what I fought 'e was supposed to do, mush," roared a wit from the gallery.

"Unfortunately, ladies and gentlemen, he has disappeared completely and cannot be traced, even by Rajah Must himself.

In short, he is missing. Therefore there will be a brief musical interlude in the programme while a thorough search is made. Thank you."

Automatically, several patrons looked underneath their tip-up seats and among the curtains surrounding the orchestra, while many of the men left their wives to see if he was hiding in the licensed bars, which quickly became packed to capacity with searchers. One lady was heard to remark that the show must go on, and they could look for Honners afterwards. Several stage-hands were dismantling the dais on which the coffin rested, and Rajah Must was shouting down an aperture in the floor in case his victim had descended to the bowels of the earth. A subterranean voice told us that "'E ain't down 'ere either, Charlie, unless 'e slipped down the plug-'ole into the drains."

"Have you checked under the orchestra and dressing-rooms?"

"Yus, Charlie—and all the lavs. Bert's doing the boiler-house and the prop stores."

The theatre manager came once more to the centre of the stage. "Ladies and gentlemen, I regret to inform you that so far our search of these vast premises has been to no avail. However, rest assured that every effort is being made to locate our young friend, and the management thanks you for your indulgence at the delay in the entertainment. Meanwhile, the show must go on. Therefore it gives me much pleasure to announce the next act. Thank you."

I sat there as one in a dream, trying to grasp the situation as the curtain rose on Gloria Frampton, one of the top singing stars of the day, as though nothing was amiss. I stared incredulously at the empty seat beside me, feeling that the whole affair was some nightmare from which I should soon awaken. The audience, Gaynor and Carmen included, were concentrating on Gloria Frampton with that intent expression of pleasure she always evoked, as her powerful voice flooded the theatre, aided by superb bust movements. An artiste from head to toe, Gloria covered the stage, flashing those dark eyes from pit to gallery, embracing the entire audience in her arms and occasionally emphasizing the lyric by pointing to individuals, thus confirming her reputation on the billboards that 'Gloria Sings For You—And You Alone.' As far as Honners was concerned, it seemed the general opinion was 'Out of sight, out of mind'. I experienced a vague feeling that perhaps they lost a member of the audience every night during Rajah Must's act, and were therefore not unduly perturbed.

It was not until Gloria's third ballad that Honners was brought to mind. As she sang *I Hear You Calling Me,* there came a muffled reply of "About time too! I've been shrieking my head off all through *Has Anyone Here Seen Kelly?* but no cow takes a blind bit of notice."

"That's Honners' voice!" I gasped, as Gloria stopped dead in full trill. Even the band went silent and everybody peered up to the flies. I stood excitedly, yelling "Is that you, Honners?" with cupped hands.

We heard "Who the devil do you think it is—Father Christmas?"

"Where are you?"

"How the hell do I know? Unless I'm stuck down a gun barrel. Get me out before I lose my temper—that's about all there is left of me!"

I climbed on the stage, where Rajah Must and the manager joined me. The three of us put our ears to the boards as if we were on a badger hunt. "Can you knock?" I shouted.

"Knock! I'm not waiting at the back door, you know. Knock! I can hardly breathe, let alone knock, you stupid oaf."

"Then shout as often as possible so we can trace you."

"Would it help if I sang you a song instead? Like *Don't Go Down The Mine, Daddy.*"

"Are you underneath the stage?"

"How the devil do I know where I am? I'm stuck in a kind of flue-pipe, and if it wasn't pitch dark I'd be able to tell if I'm upside-down or not."

"Are you hurt, Honners?"

"Oh no! Apart from breaking every bone in my body when that sooty-faced imposter let the bottom of the coffin fall open so I could plummet unexpectedly to my death, I've never been so fit since a horse flattened me at my first point-to-point."

"Are you in pain?"

"Only when I laugh. Fortunately it's much better when I try to move—I merely go unconscious. Anyhow, I'm glad to hear the show going on as if nothing has happened. Don't try to rescue me till Sunday—it might be bad for business. I'll lie quiet and not interrupt the human foghorn who's on now. And tell Rajah Must that he won't be in the theatre much longer, once I get out—he's due for a booking with his ancestors."

"We're all trying to locate you right now, Honners. Keep talking so we can pinpoint you."

Already the stage-hands were pulling up boards along the centre whence Honners' voice seemed to come, then the manager lowered himself below. Peering down, I saw the manager alight on a kind of square pipe which he tapped with the end of a torch. "Are you in there, Honners?" he called.

There came an answering tap, followed by "That's me! Get to work with a tin-opener, unless you can force the lid off this elongated biscuit tin."

The manager stared up at us. "No wonder we couldn't find him—he's stuck in the main air-conditioning shaft! Fetch spanners and wrenches from the boiler-room, Percy, and we'll take out this section. Hurry up. . . ."

"Now I know why it's so damned draughty in here," Honners observed.

Within ten minutes a twelve-foot section of ventilation shaft

144

was freed from the system and raised to the stage with Honners inside. Willing hands supported the shaft till it stood vertical, then, taking their time from the manager, raised and lowered the shaft many times in order to shake Honners out of his trap. Eventually his body, stiff and blackened, emerged from the aperture, to fall supine on the floor, gasping the words "Corned beef!"

A doctor from the audience examined Honners immediately and pronounced him remarkably free from injury, apart from a nasty head bruise. Gaynor forced a double brandy down his throat, while Rajah Must explained how Honners' small size had unfortunately resulted in his being sucked into the ventilation shaft instead of taking the normal route through the escape hatch from the coffin. "Of course, it is a chance in a million, performing the trick with one so tiny—no normal human being could possibly enter such a shaft. Nevertheless, we shall at once take measures to ensure that the risk is eliminated," he assured us. "A protective grill must be fitted to the duct entrance before the next performance."

"Tell that sooty-faced swab there won't be a next performance," Honners informed the men who were carrying him to the manager's office. "He'll learn that you can't dump a Pilkington-Goldberg down a blessed flue-pipe and live to draw your pension. Oh, that I should come to this, a black-faced refugee from a tin blowpipe!"

One of the stage-hands grinned. "Lucky you didn't fall down the 'ole in winter, mush—the 'ot 'eat would 'ave killed yer."

"Silence, you asinine flunkey! I may be a charred stiff at the moment but we Pilkington-Goldbergs have always been bred to smile at adversity. Note the courageous smirk now—if you can find the right end of me for facial grimace."

"Then why didn't you shout for help earlier on, mate?"

"First, by no stretch of your minute imagination could I

possibly be your mate. Second, even a macaroni of the blood such as myself experiences some difficulty in the matter of oral communication when he is unconscious at one end and has one foot in the grave at the other—though legend has it that one of my illustrious ancestors, Sir Foster de Pilkington—or Foster the Foolhardy as he was called—continued arguing with Henry the Eighth about his taxes despite the handicap of having had his head cut off during the audience."

"Who are you then—the Black Prince?"

"For your information, you have the honour of carting the sooty remains of the 10th Earl Apparent to the manager's office, where you will witness the historic death-bed scene of a nobleman and record his last words for posterity—'Fire this bum on the spot for insolence to his betters'."

Honners was obviously well on the way to recovery.

NINE

Despite Honners' threat to take the case of Rajah Must to the High Court and then to the House of Lords if necessary, it was remarkable how willing he was to withdraw the action when the manager of the theatre proposed a settlement of £25 plus a new suit. £25 was a fortune to us in those days, especially as Honners had hinted to me in confidence that if necessary he would settle out of court for a fiver rather than follow the example of his ancestor, Sir Maurice de Goldberg—Miser Maurice as he was known—who had spent thirty years of his life, six of them in the Tower of London, over a lawsuit to recover the cost of a duck's egg taken from his lands by Edward the First during a stag hunt. I had long learned that whatever we did, Honners' forebears had an example to match it from the distant past, where they seemed to have been placed by Destiny to alter the course of history by opposing the Crown at every turn and dropping dead in their tracks as a result. For instance, when Honners won the school chess tournament he told the Headmaster that it was a minor feat compared with the exploits of Sir Leonard de Pilkington—Leonard the Lance as he was popularly known—who had been voted Top Knight of 1483, only to be killed at Bosworth two years later through charging the army of Richard the Third minus his horse.

At school, Honners shone at History, being the constant scourge in the life of Mr Lake, our teacher in that subject.

Mr Lake's chief aim in the lessons was to pursue the syllabus and keep Honners' ancestors out of it—an almost impossible task, because the Pilkington-Goldbergs had swarmed through the past like ants, being present at all major events such as the signing of Magna Carta, The Gunpowder Plot and the Charge of the Light Brigade. Even when, in desperation, Mr Lake took us back to the building of Hadrian's Wall by the Romans during the day, we were hardly surprised to learn that, according to Honners, his family were pulling it down during the night.

Mr Lake eyed Honners icily. "One can only presuppose that your ubiquitous ancestors also provided most of the material for our Bible—unless you are about to claim that they wrote it as well."

"Oh no, sir. Our family archives only go back to the Roman occupation of Britain, I'm sorry to say. Our family records are extremely well documented from the Battle of Hastings onwards. In fact, we led the celebrated charge that decided the victory that evening just as we advised Wolfe to storm Quebec in 1759."

"Just a moment, young man. You told the class that you were fighting for King Harold in 1066, having marched post-haste from your massacre of the Danes at Stamford Bridge. According to you, Harold's personal bodyguard, the huscarles, was composed almost entirely of Pilkington-Goldbergs."

Honners smirked superiorly. "With great respect, sir, we were fighting on both sides in a manner of speaking. The Pilkingtons supported Harold, of course, but the other branch of our illustrious family, the Goldbergs, were Normans. Thus it was impossible for us to lose. However, seeing which side their bread was buttered, the wily Pilkingtons later became united to the Goldbergs by marriage, so following our famous precept laid down by Simon Pilkington—Simon the Insatiable, or, as King Alfred dubbed him after reading the census figures for A.D. 883, the Father of Wessex. It runs thus: If from field of battle fledde, daughter woo and fight in bedde. Ye certain answer to defeats, be victory won between ye sheets."

Mr Lake looked down his nose. "If I may say so, Honners, you appear to be unnaturally obsessed with the minute details —often irrelevant details—of history"

Honners drew himself up to his full lack of stature. "I am history!" he declaimed dramatically. "You see standing before your very eyes four foot of condensed honour and tradition, like they have to use gallons of milk to make a pound of butter. Observe closely the aristocratic mug staring up at you now and giving me a stiff neck into the bargain, then consider that unbroken line of Pilkington-Goldbergs stretching back over the centuries who are shrewdly weighing you up through my eyes, calculating your social rank, financial position, moral character and academic ability. The mind can barely grasp the implications, sir."

"Fortunately mine can, Honners, because glinting down at you from my own eyes are the receding columns of Lakes—notorious through history for their perception of character and vindictive natures when confronted by impudent upstarts."

"With great respect, sir, we have never heard of the Lakes on the upper deck, so to speak. Were they churls—or perhaps villeins?"

"They were—and are—schoolmasters, Honners. While your family were pillaging Europe, and later the Empire, we were endeavouring to keep a little culture and learning going on the side, just clear of your blood bath. However, that is by the way. In view of your morbid enthusiasm for the past I take it that you will be pursuing the School Cert. in History?"

"Sir, I shall never run after Brenda Baker under any circumstances. I leave her to Pook."

"Wayward youth, you deliberately misunderstand me. I refer to History as your main subject in the examinations."

"Oh yes, sir, indeed. I have no qualms whatsoever. For example, quite by accident I happened to glance at your notes which were lying open on your desk, sir, and observed that we shall soon be considering the celebrated affair between Queen Elizabeth and the Earl of Essex, with particular reference to the coded letters which passed between them. Now Walter—as we called him when he stayed at Cudford Hall with my people for the odd week-ends—wrote several of those letters in our drawing-room, which we still call the Essex Room. Sometimes he would make a mess of the code to Q.E., crumple the paper and throw it to the floor. Sir Hubert de Pilkington noticed this and made a point of collecting such litter—none of our family ever threw away anything except bills—with a view to a bit of court blackmail should opportunity offer, but that is another story. What concerns us here is that I will bring some of these letters along to our History sessions for the class to examine, with your permission of course, sir—thus bringing a refreshing breath of living History into our valuable but dry-as-dust lectures you give us, sir."

"I take your point, Honners, and as we have already wasted so much time this morning, let us return immediately to my dry-as-dust lecture on the Domesday Book of 1086 by turning to your notes on the subject. Yes, Honners? You wish to ask a question?"

"I merely wanted to point out, sir, that Sir Randolph Pilkington—Randolph the Reticent as he was called—refused adamantly to reveal any facts or figures to William for the census relating to Domesday, declaring it to be a flagrant invasion of privacy. That is why there is a blank space against the Manor of Cudford, except under the heading of oxen and pigs, where it is written 'A mighty assemble of ye oxen and ye pigges, ye nombre of whyche is notte knowne'. Followed by an entry in my ancestors own hand, thus: 'And never shall be, though I kill evrie fat-bellied Norman whosoever poketh his nose over my walls'."

"Don't tell me that by a strange coincidence you happen to have the Domesday Book tucked away in your satchel, you obnoxious little snob," Mr Lake hissed dangerously. "Let me warn you—one more word on that score or another reference to those blasted ancestors of yours, and you'll join them in Hell! Speak at your peril, young man."

"I may be obnoxious, sir, but certainly not a snob; I speak

to anyone, as is patent right now. . . ."

"Shut up!"

"Peasant!" Honners whispered to me vehemently. "My family used to hire his kind by the gross—to flatten the soil with their big feet after barley planting. We let them think it was morris dancing, so they wouldn't know they were working and expect payment. Give old Lake a maypole to dance round and he'd eventually disappear down a circular trench. Believe me, his family have about as much tradition behind them as a plastic horseshoe."

For the beginning of our feud with Mr Lake it is necessary to go back to our first arrival at Cudford Grammar School. The Convent of the Holy Angels was so anxious to be rid of Honners that he joined Cudford Grammar School a whole term earlier than I did, which gave him a superiority he never lost.

"Cudford Grammar sent out an urgent appeal for the cream of the nation's youth, so naturally I responded immediately," Honners explained, to account for his rapid departure from the Convent of the Holy Angels, despite Reverend Mother's hint that the Convent was no place for fallen angels.

At that time Mr Lake took us for Geography—dubbed by us as the study of the British Empire, plus the other little bit we don't mention in public—only to discover that whatever country he examined, Honners' family had either captured it, colonized it or lost it. Honners contradicted Mr Lake's assertion that there had been misrule in Ceylon, on the grounds that his great-uncle, Sir William Pilkington-Goldberg, was Governor at the time, thereby making any suggestion of misrule unthinkable. On the contrary, everybody knew that this particular era had been noteworthy for its unprecedented and inspired leadership in the shape of William the Wise. A first class row developed in the classroom between Mr Lake and Honners over Ceylon, especially when the master insisted that the corrupt administration of the Governor should have earned him the title of William the Wonky. We witnessed the unique case of both master and pupil threatening to report each other to the Headmaster—one for insolence, and the other for the more serious charge of sedition to the Crown. Having brought Queen Victoria into the argument, Honners addressed the ceiling, imploring her late Majesty to observe the results of his father's tragic attack of democracy on the brain which had prompted him to send Honners to Cudford Grammar School instead of Harrow, thus exposing him to the unscrupulous attacks of an undetected Bolshevik.

Both Mr Lake and Honners had separate interviews with the Headmaster that very day, with the result that at our next Geography lesson Mr Lake announced that he had abandoned Ceylon and, as a last resort, was about to take us out into space to study the Solar System.

"Assuming for the moment that your relations have not yet been able to annex the planets, Honners, I shall be obliged if Pook will inform the class where the Earth is to be found."

"What a question!" I complained, hastily hiding my copy of *Boxing* under the desk. "Most of it is dumped in the fields, sir. The farmers keep it outdoors to stick the wheat in so they can cut it more easily. Sometimes they have too much, so they pile it up for hills. Indoors they call it mud."

"Stupid youth! I mean locate the Earth in the Solar System, of course."

"Why, has it got blocked up, sir?" I found it so difficult to fit school work into my own life of physical education that I seldom knew what Mr Lake was talking about, so I did not listen more than I could help.

"We are not discussing the drains, Pook. I am aware that you live in a fantasy world of inflated muscles and bloody combats, but surely even you know what the Solar System is."

"Is it anything to do with the solar plexus? I know all about that in boxing."

"The connection is so remote that life is too short to pursue it. Instead, we shall have a practical demonstration by reconstructing the Solar System in the classroom. Poole shall sit on the radiator and represent the sun; Parker, Parsley and Pitt will be Mercury, Venus and Mars in that order. These are known as the inner planets, with the addition of Earth. Pook shall be Earth and I want Honners to stand close to him as the moon—the lunar satellite whence we derive our word lunatic. Now class, cast your shallow minds back many million years ago to an era when even the Pilkington-Goldbergs had not yet crawled out of the primeval slime, when the moon did not exist. We believe that a large portion of the Earth's matter became detached from an area we now recognize as the Pacific Ocean and was thrown off into space to become the moon, thus."

Mr Lake gave Honners such a kick in the pants that my friend shot across the room with a howl of surprise. "Honners is now in orbit round the Earth, some 240,000 miles from Pook. He must now walk round Pook, each circuit representing 27 days, 7 hours and 43 minutes, roughly corresponding to our month, at the same time revolving on his own axis."

"How the hell do I do that?" Honners demanded angrily, but remembering Dr.Windebank's lecture during the recent interview about good behaviour or dying under the lash.

"Just watch Pook, Honners. He is circling Poole the sun once every 365 days, 6 hours—our year—and at the same time revolving on his own axis once every 24 hours—our day. Simply rotate on your toes as you would in an old-fashioned waltz."

"What am I supposed to be, a scholar or a human top?" Honners grumbled. "All this is completely opposed to the latest trends in child psychology. I should like to know what Professor Swartzbaum of New York would have to say about booting kids up the backside and spinning them round the classroom. It's enough to warp my ego and embitter my subconscious for life. If I turn out a failure in my career and degenerate into a hardened criminal—even a vicious sex-killer—at least we shall know whom to blame. I need love, assistance, encouragement and sympathetic understanding during this impressionable period of adolescent development, like Professor Swartzbaum's book says."

Honners always threw Professor Swartzbaum at Mr Lake when in trouble, and Mr Lake always threw him back. "Unfortunately, Honners, Professor Swartzbaum's controversial theories do not provide for those adolescents who are failures and hardened criminals at the commencement of their school days—probably because the shelter of his ivory tower has prevented his coming into contact with the likes of Pook and your good self. May I add that my own practical experience over thirty years tells me that the only time you will ever need love, assistance and sympathetic understanding will be when we file past your coffin."

"How will that help me then, sir?"

"By taking the form of prayer on your behalf, Honners. But enough of pleasant flights of fancy and back to the Solar System. Come here, Puddle."

Puddle, the fat boy of the class, waddled over to Mr Lake, looking a most unlikely object for sending up into space.

"Now, Puddle, I want you to imagine you are a meteorite shooting through the sky. When Honners the moon reaches the apogee of his orbit, you will streak through space and crash onto his surface, thus."

Honners came rotating all unsuspecting to the apogee of his orbit, suddenly to be knocked clean off his axis by Puddle the meteorite. This violent collision propelled him like a billiard ball into Venus and thence to the floor.

"'Excellent representation, Puddle. Get to your feet, Honners, stop swearing about rugby in space, and continue to orbit as before, but note that now you have a crater on your face, so typical of the moon's pocked surface. We believe this is how the belt of asteroids between Mars and Jupiter was formed, when the then fifth planet from the sun came into collision with a large Puddle-like body and split into fragments. Keep rotating, everybody, but pay special attention to my next demonstration—the eclipse of the sun by the moon, then the eclipse of the moon by the earth, as the shadow of the earth thrown by the sun obscures the moon. Everybody follow their orbital paths until I see you are in the correct positions for the necessary penumbra. Very satisfactory so far. . . . Upon my soul, what was that crash!"

We all heard the thud from outer space and turned to see that the moon was no longer in orbit. Instead, Honners was lying motionless on his face. I ran across the classroom to turn Honners on to his back. He opened his eyes and murmured "Where the hell am I?"

Mr Lake hurried across. "Ah, merely a slight bout of vertigo, my little friend. Pook put a handkerchief to his nose to staunch the bleeding while everyone else returns to his desk for notes on our experiment. Now we'll carry our dizzy old moon to his own desk and in next to no time he'll be right as rain."

Honners sat in his seat in the pose I had seen so often—head right back and one hand clasping a handkerchief to the nostrils—while he informed the ceiling that an unnamed idiot in a black gown who had obviously escaped from Cudford Asylum was rapidly earning himself the fate of being shot by night in his padded cell."

"Careful, Honners," Mr Lake warned. "We don't want another interview with Dr Windebank just yet, eh?"

"Not unless he asks me to tell the warders where you're hiding," Honners mumbled through the handkerchief. "Everybody knows I'm as delicate as porcelain, yet they subject me to indoor rugby masquerading as modern educational methods. If that's supposed to be astral geography then give me good old-fashioned judo any day—at least you can fight back. Why, my doctor won't even let me go on roundabouts at the fair, in case I have a stroke, so heaven knows what he'd say if he knew I was compelled to spin round and round a room like a blessed gyroscope out of control. Even when a bus goes round a sharp bend I black out and siphon what little life blood there's left all over the floor. . . ."

"Shut up, Honners, and give your nose a chance to. . . ."

"I can't help it if I am so finely bred that I'm cursed with a leaky faucet where other folks have a nose. The miracle is that I'm still alive to sue that educational nut-case before he murders the lot of us. Feel in my pocket for the cotton wool, then bung some up both nostrils, for pity's sake. I'll see the school Governors and have old Windebank down to assistant care-taker when I've finished with this lot . . . Oh my gawd!"

Honners opened his eyes, to find himself staring into the cold mask of Dr Windebank himself.

"Hearing a great deal of bad-tempered shouting from this classroom, I entered to find our young friend having yet another fit of tantrums," Dr Windebank remarked icily. "Explain your conduct, Honners."

Honners laughed falsely. "Only acting, sir. Rehearsing the school play, sir. Working up a scene of difficult drama."

"Such as Dostoievsky's *Crime and Punishment?*"

"Oh no, sir—more like *Much Ado About Nothing.*"

"Is this boy telling me the truth, Mr Lake?"

Mr Lake rubbed his hands and smiled contentedly, then slowly shook his head.

"I see. Come with me, Honners, to my study. There I shall stop your nose-bleed by applying a counter-irritant to your other end. Tell the class what motto hangs on the wall of my room."

" 'Don't be vague—ask for Haig,' sir."

"Idiot! That is the calendar next to it, kindly presented to me by the famous whisky distillers. You know as well as I do that is not a motto. Try again, boy."

"Sorry, sir—I thought it was your motto. I think the one next to it says 'To err is human; to forgive, divine.' It's my favourite too, sir—Alexander Pope knew his stuff."

"Are you incapable of telling the truth, boy? That is the last motto I should choose, with you on roll. Hanging on my wall is the much sounder recommendation of Samuel Butler's —'Spare the rod, and spoil the child.' Follow me at once to my study, where we shall put this worthy advice into practice without delay."

Honners was visibly shaken—not surprising in view of Dr Windebank's notorious flogging power—and began to play his last card, not so much a trump as a feeble little deuce.

"With great respect, sir, Samuel Butler appears to be ordering us to spare the rod and spoil the child. Spare the rod by all means, sir, but you don't actually have to spoil me."

"Don't make it worse for yourself by stupid illogicalities, boy. In your precocious manner you are always telling us how the Pilkington-Goldbergs have been brought up to regard pain as a form of pleasure—therefore come now and enjoy yourself."

"But, sir, think of the risk involved. Last time you practically bashed my legs off my torso. Surely you don't want me to die all over your best carpet, sir? Think of the good name of our school, sir."

"Every time I thrash you, boy, rest assured that the good name of our school is uppermost in my mind. My sole aim is to beat it into *your* mind. Come."

As Honners left his desk he whispered to me, "Sadist! If the police find any pulp in his study, tell them it's me."

At the end of my first term at Cudford Grammar School, Honners announced airily, "We old hands always stage a pretty big rag to celebrate the closing of the jail for the vacation.

"Such as?" I inquired.

"Well, I think it's high time we gave that commoner Lake something to remember us by."

"Like burning his books or letting his tyres down?"

"We've done all that before, so why repeat. No, Peter, I've got a better plan. You know the pride of his life is his look-out tower in the classroom—well it's symbolic of the old fool, so it'll have to go."

The object in question was the rostrum or high desk from which Mr Lake surveyed the class after mounting four steps to reach his perch—known to us as his look-out tower. It was a sturdy piece of mahogany furniture some six feet tall, and mounted on castors in case it needed to be moved. It appeared particularly massive to Honners, who made a point of referring to it in his conversations with Mr Lake as Windsor Castle. When Mr Lake mislaid his spectacles, it was always Honners who said, "I'm used to heights, sir, so stay on the ground while I climb to the top of Windsor Castle and see if they are lying on the battlements."

"Even with Puddle and Parsley we couldn't carry the lookout tower downstairs," I pointed out, "It weighs a ton."

"No need to, Peter. There's a much easier, and certainly quicker way—through the window."

"That's even more ridiculous. We'd never hold a weight like that on a rope—supposing it would go through the window anyway, which I doubt."

"I've measured, and it will fit nicely," Honners asserted smugly. "And who said anything about a rope?"

"Well, if we don't use a rope it will smash to pieces on the asphalt playground below—we're three storeys up, remember."

"Fancy that, now! Who would have thought Lake's old rostrum would smash to pieces from only three storeys up! What ever next!"

"When did you manage to measure up then, Honners?"

"I did the whole job during Maths, when Lake had us at what he calls Practical Mensuration, right under his long nose. After I had taped the window dimensions, I actually asked him if I could measure Windsor Castle, on the excuse that I wanted to work out its volume. You want the best nerves—I've got 'em."

"What about Puddle and Parsley?"

"They're already in, under an oath of secrecy that if they blab I shall personally slit their throats open like zippers."

On the last day of term, after final assembly, the four of us hid in the toilet until the school was deserted. At 4.30 p.m., we made our way up to the classroom for the big push, as Honners called it. All hands pulled the rostrum to a chalk mark Honners had made on the floor, then Puddle raised the big window overlooking the playground. Next, the four of us slowly tilted the rostrum towards the window, Puddle and Parsley holding the top and lowering it carefully on to the window-sill. When this position had been achieved, it required all four of us to lift the base so the rostrum was horizontal to the floor. All we had to do now was to slide it over the window-sill into space. The better to accomplish this heavy work, Honners sang his own special tower-sliding shanty, as he called it, which went:

> 'Think of beauty, think of love,
> Think of Lake and really shove.
> Think of school, think of bell,
> Think of Lake and push like hell.
> Think of coal, think of cinder,
> Windsor Castle's through the winder.'

On the last line the rostrum freed itself from our grip, to float and turn on its journey to the ground. We stretched out to savour the spectacle to the utmost, but even we had not bargained for the impact when it hit the asphalt. There was a kind of explosion and Mr Lake's rostrum suddenly disappeared as such, its previous existence being marked only by firewood scattered thinly here and there about the playground. Puddle emitted a boyish oath and turned his pale face to mine.

"It went off like a bloomin' bomb!" he gasped.

Honners was the first one to recover his wits. "Mission completed, men. Operation Watch-Tower one hundred per cent successful. Return to base."

Excitedly we followed Honners down the stairs, in pursuance of his well-laid plans. Our escape was effected by keeping to the covered route via the junior school toilets, the science lab and the cycle sheds, until we gained the school wall where we could climb over unobserved behind the gym. Immediately Puddle and Parsley run-jumped a moving tram, while Honners and I scuttled down Drift Alley where we could merge with the market crowds. Honners' face glowed with satisfaction at the thrill of adventure and the success of his scheme.

"That'll teach old Lake that you can't cross swords with the Pilkington-Goldbergs and live to wear Windebank's presentation Mckey Mouse watch when they cart you out of the classroom on retirement and dump you in the nearest pub. Byebye, Peter—have fun."

Almost as soon as we separated for the vacation, the rostrum incident was wiped from my mind with the forgetfulness of youth. Far more important to me was the fact that I had won the Junior School boxing tournament in my first term as a lightweight. Being a supremely confident child, I had written my name on the entry lists for all five weights, until, just as I was about to do the same for the eight weights of the Senior School, the sports master informed me that even the Cudford Infant was allowed to enter for only one weight—my own; 9 stones 9 pounds. I won with ease in this division, but felt cheated that I had been restricted to one silver cup when thirteen trophies were available.

When the school entered the Great Hall for the first assembly of the new term, I was delighted to see the thirteen silver cups arrayed on the Headmaster's table in the centre of the stage. Sitting all round were the forty-odd masters in cap and gown, flanked on one side by the choir and on the other side by the prefects. Everybody stood when Dr Windebank entered the silent hall, and studied his mask of a face in a vain endeavour to divine the mood of the day.

Without any preliminaries Dr Windebank made an opening announcement. "Peter Pook will come to the stage immediately."

I glanced at my chums and smiled confidently. "He's not going to waste any time presenting me with the boxing cup," I whispered. I quickly mounted the stage and stood proudly by the glittering cups.

Then Dr Windebank boomed "Pilkington-Goldberg will now come to the stage." As Honners made his way up I thought to myself that there must be some mistake. Honners had been in the competition at junior paper-weight, but he had been disqualified in the very first bout for biting his opponent in the clinch. He certainly wasn't due for a cup.

I looked sideways at Honners, who whispered cocksuredly, "Seems as though Windebank's going to hand over the Junior Chess Shield to me right away." Then I remembered Honners' victory in the school chess tournament of last term.

Next, Dr Windebank called up Parsley. I racked my brains to think what Parsley had won, then recalled that he had come top in the class maths' examination. I felt that Parsley deserved not only the class prize but also a vote of thanks from me because I had copied large chunks of my own answers from his paper.

But when Dr Windebank summoned Puddle to the stage I thought about his talents in vain. He just didn't have any. Puddle was too lazy to work, too fat to fight and too short of breath to run. In fact, nature seemed to have fashioned Puddle merely to fill the bottom place in whatever he undertook, like a ready-made floor. Surely we hadn't sunk to awarding a prize for the biggest appetite? Even Honners was staring at Puddle with a puzzled expression, as if a rhino was lining up for the start of the Derby.

I seldom listened to Dr Windebank's celebrated homilies from the platform, exhorting the citizens of tomorrow to stop being juvenile playboys and rush out from Cudford Grammar School to rebuild the world which his own generation had made such a mess of. This theme had been christened by Honners as Windebank's bricklayers' speech on behalf of the building trade, and when the Headmaster referred to us as future Empire builders Honners made cement-and-trowel motions which we understood to be associated with a near-by development site where the new Empire Cinema was in course of construction. Dr Windebank little suspected that his lectures were accompanied by a running commentary from Honners, thus:

"So what do I mean when I call you boys Empire builders?"
"Irish brickies."
"And where will be your sphere of action?"
"Middle Street, next to Marks and Spencers."
"Again, consider the mighty institution you will serve."
"Merrick's Building Works."
"And the results of your labours."
"Biggest cinema in Cudford."
"Now, what do you require for such an undertaking?"
"Hod, trowel, and three-to-one sand and cement."
"And where will you spend your well-deserved furloughs?"
"In the Bold Forester."
"And what will lesser men think of you, then?"
"Sloshed."
"But when your task is completed—what next?"

"Pull it down. They really wanted a dance hall."

"So why must you gird up your loins and start again?"

"Fired for not wearing braces."

"Once more you will turn your eyes east of Suez."

"Through the window of Cudford Labour Exchange."

"And what then will be your most pressing need?"

"More bricks."

"As you survey the Empire on which the sun never sets?"

"Sun-glasses."

"Dare we anticipate posterity's verdict on you?"

"Dead as mutton."

"In conclusion, boys, let us consider how a grateful Mother-land will reward you sons of the Empire."

"Free burial."

"And try to imagine the status of your proud children."

"Orphans."

"Therefore what inspiring lesson have we learned from our discourse this morning?"

"Don't be a brickie."

"Thus I sincerely trust I have implanted in your impression-able young minds the desire for the greatest of all gifts in our national heritage."

"Money."

"In the hope that you will stride onwards towards that other glorious goal for which our forefathers strove all their lives in the name of king and country."

"Women."

Honners ceaseless little tongue never knew when to stop, but this morning I noticed that Dr Windebank had abandoned the Empire in favour of the Goths and Vandals. The barbaric hordes from the East were galloping through Europe under the leadership of Gunderic, crossing the Pyrenees and spreading throughout the West. In A.D. 428 80,000 of them under Genseric crossed to North Africa; then at a much later date they moved into Britain. This particular band of Vandals, I was surprised to learn, settled in Cudford, where they wrought great havoc despite their small numbers. I was even more shocked to learn that their names were Pook, Pilkington-Goldberg, Parsley and Puddle.

Honners was the first to recover his wits when the implications of Dr Windebank's oration dawned on us. "I must protest most strongly, sir, at being called a Vandal. On the contrary, I am descended from a mixture of pure Saxon and Norman stock—Saxon because the Pilkingtons were. . . ."

"Silence, boy!" Dr Windebank roared angrily. "Mr Lake, be so kind as to display the first exhibit of evidence against these Vandals."

Mr Lake rose in the hushed hall and drew a cloth off a pile, revealing the bundled remains of his rostrum neatly stacked like firewood.

"Now, Pilkington-Goldberg, since you appear to know so much, tell the school what that is," Dr Windebank thundered."

"Wood, sir."

"Exactly, boy. Perhaps you will be so kind as to tell the school what it was before that."

"A tree, sir."

"Very well, first a tree and now wood. Can you remember what it was between those two stages?"

"Planks, sir."

"And then?"

"A lifeboat, sir?"

"May I assist your memory by inquiring what a lifeboat would be doing in your classroom, boy?—and don't you dare tell me it was washed up there on a wave of enthusiasm."

"Something to do with our Sea Scouts, sir?"

"And they decided to launch the craft from the window, perhaps, eh?"

"No sea, sir."

"No indeed, boy, no sea—and no truth either. Craddock, come to the stage, please."

Craddock, our junior school caretaker, appeared in his best suit and stood respectfully on the stage. At a nod from the Headmaster he said, "In the normal performance of me duties I was freeing a blocked waste-pipe in the kitchens, when me attention was drawn by a loud noise from the playground. Rising quickly from me blocked waste-pipe I looked through the window and perceived large quantities of timber dropping about the asphalt. Looking upwards I sees faces leaning out of a top winder. Immediately I proceeded to room 8, only to find it empty. Next, I looks out of the open winder and eventually sees four boys disappearing behind the gym. I turns to give chase and notices Mr Lake's rostrum. It ain't there. I hurries downstairs to the gym but the boys ain't there either."

"Thank you, Craddock. Were you able to identify the four boys in question?"

"Yes, sir. They was Pook, Pilkington-Goldberg, Parsley and Puddle. Them four there, sir."

"That will be all, Craddock. You may return to your duties. Now, Pilkington-Goldberg, in the light of Craddock's evidence what do you say?"

"Incredibly bad grammar, sir. Personally, I could not possibly place much credence on such distorted English."

"Ignoring that red-herring, I shall be surprised if even you will contest such damning proof."

"Full of elementary loopholes, sir. It may be necessary for me to request the services of my uncle, Sir James Pilkington-Goldberg, K.C., to conduct my defence. He is celebrated throughout the legal profession as James the Just, sir."

"I think that course of action will hardly be required, boy, unless your uncle is available during the next ten minutes. The position is that either you own up or receive immediate expulsion from Cudford Grammar School. Now how do you plead?"

"Guilty, m'lud."

"Although we are not actually in the Old Bailey, I accept your plea. Now, tell me what is the greatest prerogative of our ancient legal system?

"Mercy, sir."

"No, idiot!—justice. Messrs. Hall, Cooper, Fanshaw and Reid, kindly step forward, that justice may not only be done but may be seen to be done."

The four sports masters—all ex-rugby blues—walked to the centre of the stage carrying canes. Honners eyed Mr Cooper with horror, staring up to the top of his 6' 4" stature. Dr Windebank ordered the four of us to bend over for punishment.

"I submit to a public flogging, sir," Honners gasped, "because we Pilkington-Goldbergs are stoics right through to our boots, but in my case there is some danger that you may not so much cane me as drive me out of the building like a golf-ball. In view of my size, sir, I think you will agree to the imposition of 500 lines instead. . . ."

"Bend over, boy!"

The sound of the public flogging reminded me of rifle fire in a shooting gallery, as the four of us were beaten simultaneously in front of the whole school. The pain was immense but none of us wept. The only noise came from Honners, who gasped something about his legs being severed from his body by a cheese-cutter. When we walked painfully back to our places in the body of the hall he informed our class that it would be necessary for him to go through life minus his buttocks, which had now completely disappeared, though medical examination would probably locate them sticking out of his stomach like knees.

Despite Honners' gloomy prediction—based on the child psychology of Professor Swartzbaum—that the flogging had caused deep mental and psychological disturbances within him which would undoubtedly wreck his adult life, none of us engaged in vandalism again or appeared any the worse for the ordeal. We made public apology to Mr Lake and our parents were billed for the cost of a new rostrum, but, as one might expect, the final comment on the incident came from Honners himself.

"When Scotland Yard is hunting the schizophrenic psychopath whom society tortured into his present condition and then rejected, I shall make sure that old Lake is the first victim of my unnatural blood lust. Meanwhile, in order to raise funds for my future, I am going to exhibit the complex track lay-out of Clapham junction now permanently engraved on my backside for the modest sum of sixpence a look."

There were no takers.

TEN

Even the great freezeup—the worst in living memory—failed to interfere with Olga's courtship programme. Having swept the snow off the seat, we sat in our usual place in the shelter on Cudford Common for that strange type of juvenile pleasure known to Olga as the rites of love. This consisted in holding each other like bundles for two hours without speaking and staring out into the darkness like coastguards on a moonless night.

I gazed at the starry heavens, wondering if I too was sitting out there in the icy wastes of space, slowly freezing to death. We had learnt in Physics lessons that molecular energy stops at -230 degrees Centigrade, although oxygenation of the blood ceases completely far above that temperature of absolute zero, but it was not until tonight that I really appreciated the significance of these figures.

When we spoke, our breath issued forth in vapoury spurts, like visible sound waves. "I think I've got hypothermia," I gasped as the distant chimes of Cudford Town Hall recorded that we had done our two hours vigil.

"What's that, Peter—intense sexual excitement?" Olga whispered hopefully.

"It's a state of extreme cold, when the metabolism of the body ceases completely and your limbs start to drop off. We read about it in Physics at school. I don't want to alarm you, dear, but I'm passing away in your arms."

"I thought you were unusually cold tonight, Peter."

"That is a joke in the poorest taste, Olga. I honestly can't feel a thing."

Olga giggled. "Just as well, you naughty boy. Come closer and I'll warm you up—though you've got enough clothes on to stock a shop."

How I could possibly get any closer to my beloved without

breaking her open like a packing-case was beyond me. I began to tremble all over, and this rapid movement transmitted itself to Olga until she began to shake in time with me. We clung to each other as though we were marooned on a mechanical agitator. Worst of all I couldn't feel my lips. I extracted a hand to find them but the fingers were so numb that it was necessary to look in order to see if they were in contact with my lips. I passed my hand over my face and experienced that eerie feeling of nothingness one has after a dentist's injection.

"Kiss me, Peter," Olga whispered, closing her eyes and lolling her head back in the conventional pose of surrender.

"How?" I gasped.

"Oh, you're not much fun tonight, Peter. Kiss me or I'll know you don't love me any more."

"Wait a minute then, while I massage my lips." Desperately I rubbed my dead lips, then tried to pull them forward into position with my fingers.

"Silly, you can't kiss me with your nose, Peter. Come up a bit. That's better."

"Can you feel anything?"

"Of course I can. Can't you?"

"Not a thing, even when I bite my lip."

"Oh my! It really sounds as though you've got frostbite. Perhaps we'd better go to the café for something hot. How are your legs?"

"What legs?" I said this seriously, certain that I ended abruptly at the pelvis.

"I can't understand you, Peter. Ronald never felt the cold when he was with me."

"He must have been an Eskimo." Like most girls, Olga spent much of her life in a fantasy world, hotly pursued by Ronald, the Perfect Man. Although nobody had ever met Ronald, I had grown to hate him over the years, for he seemed to be a combination of true gentleman, generous fool and servile

169

slave—possessing all the virtues I lacked.

"If Ronald's so blooming wonderful why don't you marry him and have done with it—then I could come and live with you both rent free. Don't waste time with a normal human being like me."

"He keeps on asking me to marry him but I don't want to disappoint you, Peter. Besides, people would only say I was after his money."

"Then why be afraid of the truth?"

"Oh, you're horrid, Peter. Ronald never says nasty things like that to me."

"I don't suppose he does. He's probably too busy smiling into your eyes like a half-wit as he carries you into café after café to try and fill you up."

"Oh, Peter, anyone would think I was a big eater."

"You're not, dear—compared with an elephant."

"I shall ignore that. Now let's get going, and on the way we can test the ice to see if it's all right for skating on tomorrow."

"At this temperature it must be frozen right to the bottom."

We walked across Cudford Lake to improve my circulation, then Olga said, "Do you really think it'll be safe for us all to skate tomorrow, Peter?"

"Safe? Why, you could drive an army tank across. Look." To prove my point I jumped up and down several times and went through the ice up to my waist.

"Oh dear, you fell in, Peter," Olga cried. "What a blessing you tested it properly or we might have had a serious accident tomorrow."

"What do you think we've had tonight, you daft witch. You might have remembered this is the end where the warm water flows in from the brewery outfall." I climbed out angry and sick with discomfort. No sooner were we on land again but my trousers froze on me as I walked, till they hung like metal drums. I felt very near the end. Olga helped me across the common to Fred's Café, where she bought me a bowl of hot soup and a lump of bread, as though I was a tramp she had found on the Embankment. Gratefully I fell on my hands and knees in the fireplace, until Fred pulled me out before I scorched.

"My word, your nose is red," she told me as I struggled to hold the spoon in my trembling hand without throwing soup all over the room. "He fell into Cudford Lake, poor thing," she added, to explain my condition to Fred. "That's why his trousers are thawing over your floor."

I felt so ill and sexless that I was toying with the idea of having Fred phone Cudford Hospital for an ambulance, especially when Olga said, "For goodness sake try to warm up –you're making the table vibrate so, you'll spill the nice hot soup. If this is your idea of a mad night of love, give me Ronald any time. At least he was hot blooded. Just look at your hair —it's all stuck out like a flue-brush."

"Of course it is—it's frozen stiff."

"Don't be silly—a little bit of frost on your head won't hurt you. Just fancy, Ronald swims when there's ice on the sea."

"You don't want a man—you want a blooming seal during the mating season. Now shut up while I try to get this soup into my mouth without wetting the people at the next table."

Seeing my predicament, Fred came across and handed me a milk straw. "No good trying to poke the soup up your nose, Peter. Use a straw and suck it. If that doesn't help, come in the kitchen and we'll put you in the oven for a bit."

Half an hour in the warm atmosphere of the café did me the power of good, although I was still wet and sniffy. At length Olga said to me, "You don't seem your old self tonight, Peter. I think you'd better come home and meet my Mum."

"But really I prefer you, dear, despite everything. In any case your mum's too old for me."

"I don't mean like that, silly. She keeps on saying it's time she met her future son-in-law."

"By the way you talk, I was under the impression he practically lives with you."

"Who do you mean?"

"Ronald, of course."

"Not Ronald, Peter—you. Come round now and we'll do something about your wet clothes before you catch pneumonia."

Olga paid the bill, then helped me over the frozen snow to her house. Inside, she found a note on the hall table, reading it aloud. " 'Aunt Flo is frozen up, so I've gone round there for the night. Back tomorrow. Love, Mum.' Oh dear, Peter, just think, we're all alone in the house—just like it will be when we're married."

Whatever we did, Olga always told me it would be just like when we were married, and I always asked "Married to whom, dear?"

"To each other, silly—I know you want to ask me but you're afraid I'll say no."

" 'But I'm barely nineteen, Olga."

"Exactly. That's three years over the age of consent. Mind you don't leave it too late and become a miserable old bachelor. Take your wet things off so I can dry them, and I'll put Vick on your chest."

"Who's he? I thought you said we were alone."

"Rub Vick on your chest, stupid. Then you can get into my bed. I want you to make a woman of me tonight, Peter."

"But surely you are a woman already? How else could you have gone to Cudford Girls' High School?"

"Just to make it all right, I've bought you a ring, Peter." Olga produced a gold ring mounted with an emerald stone. I examined it with some surprise.

"But I couldn't wear a ring like that, Olga. Admittedly it's lovely and extremely generous of you, but it's a girl's ring."

"It's not for you, Peter, but for you to give to me."

"How can I give it to you when it's yours already?" I never could follow Olga's line of thought with presents. Last Christmas she bought me a pearl necklace on the same principle, preferring it to the hammer I had made for her in metal work. Then she had me give her the necklace and I ended up with a hammer for Christmas, plus a bottle of Caveman Cologne For Men.

"Isn't it exciting, Peter!" Olga giggled, putting on the ring. "Now take your clothes off so I can dry them in the kitchen. Don't be shy—you can slip this dressing-gown on meanwhile."

"Can I come in the kitchen and warm up by the fire, dear?"

"You won't get very warm over an electric clothes-drier, Peter. The fire's up in my bedroom, so pop up there like a good boy before you catch your death."

As I gratefully soaked up the heat of Olga's fire in the bedroom it occurred to me that things were going so smoothly from Olga's point of view that if I possessed a suspicious nature I might have thought I was a pawn in a well-planned game. Olga soon returned with the air of the competent housewife and said, "Now get into bed, Peter, while I rub your chest with Vick. Then drink this hot lemon I've made you."

Apparently I could not be rubbed in without removing the dressing-gown. Furthermore, Olga seemed to be under the impression that I might develop a cough in my stomach or even in my hips, judging by the way she rubbed. "If you don't mind my saying so dear, I've never heard of anyone complain of a nasty touch of bronchitis on the knees," I protested. Surely she didn't intend doing my feet as well?

Olga laughed. "You fell in icy water, didn't you? So, there's nothing like a Vick massage to take the cold out of your poor bones. If you're still frigid after that, I'll give you a boiling-hot mustard bath, so there."

"Are we both talking about the same kind of cold, Olga?"

"Don't keep worrying, Peter—just lie back and enjoy it.

Then I'll get you a nice hot-water bottle."

With that, Olga turned off the light and I heard the sound of a zip, followed by the plop of shoes on carpet. Then somebody got in bed beside me.

"Is that you, Olga?" I whispered.

"Of course it is, silly. Who did you think it was—the doctor? I promised you'd have a hot-water bottle."

"Where is it then?"

"Oh dear—it's me!"

"But you haven't got any clothes on."

"Well, people don't usually dress up when they're going to bed, do they? We're going to sleep together for the very first time, Peter—I can't put it plainer than that, can I?"

"Shall we go to sleep now then? I hope my snore won't keep you awake."

"Peter, when lovers sleep together they don't go to sleep. Can't you understand?"

"You mean they sleep together awake? How do they do that?"

"Listen, Peter. Don't go to sleep—just let things happen naturally. Keep very quiet and think of me and I'll do the same."

"Why don't you think of me for a change, instead of yourself?"

"That's what I meant. We'll think of each other."

Thinking about Olga always sent me off to sleep, but coupled with the rigours of this evening, it made me fall into deep slumber. Olga had to shake me hard to awaken me.

"Don't go to sleep on this of all nights," she ordered sharply. "For heaven's sake try to be a bit more romantic. Kiss me as though you are mad with passion—go on."

I gave Olga a long lingering kiss, which she enjoyed immensely until she found I had dropped asleep on her face. Once more she aroused me,—and it was at that moment we both heard the noise. It sounded like bed springs and seemed to come from the adjoining bedroom.

"Oh, it's probably the ice cracking on the roof," she explained before I could inquire as to the cause. I listened for some time, then said, "I've never heard ice talking before. Is your house haunted?"

In the stillness of the night there came the vague sound of a woman's voice, as though she were talking in her sleep. Olga laughed quietly. "Do you know what it is, Peter?"

"Your mum talking in her sleep?"

"Don't be ridiculous, Peter—the house is empty. We've left the radio on. Wait here while I slip down and turn it off."

Listening intently, I gained the impression that Olga turned the radio off by telling it to shut up. Then she returned to the bedroom.

"Fancy leaving the radio on, Peter," she said, getting into bed. "Now it's all nice and quiet for you to make love to me, so let's imagine we're on our honeymoon."

Before I could reply, the voice came through the wall again. "We ought to have a nice joint of New Zealand lamb for Sunday, then Peter can come for dinner and meet the family. . . ."

"I thought you switched the radio off, Olga. In any case, they wouldn't talk about me on there. I'm sure it's your mum talking in her sleep. If it is, I'm getting out of here fast— you're trying to frame me. . . ."

Olga piped her eye and hugged me close. "Yes, Peter, the old witch won't shut up. I'm sorry, darling, but I thought you'd like a mad night of love with me."

"What about the note in the hall then?"

"I wrote it. This weather is so awful, it was the only way to make sure we were together. Don't be angry, Peter. . . ."

Before I had time to be angry there was a knock at the front door. At first we ignored it but it was repeated three times. "Must be Ronald," I suggested.

But we knew it wasn't Ronald when a familiar voice

shrieked up at the window. "Come on, Peter, open up. Urgent business. Fred told me Olga had taken you round here."

"It's Honners!" I gasped. "Ignore him and he'll go away."

We lay in bed listening to small snowballs hitting the bedroom window, until the neighbourhood was suddenly filled with the doubtful melody of Honners singing a carol. Then he shouted, "All right, Peter, I know where you are. If you won't come down, I'll climb up. Here I come."

We listened in horrified silence to the climbing noises from without, then to the oaths that followed as Honners found the drainpipe too slippery. "Blast and damnation take it, I'll have to break the door down! Just let me get hold of a brick from this rockery and I'll teach you to keep me out here in the frozen night," he screamed.

"Honners is losing his temper," I told Olga. "Wait here while I talk to him before he has all the neighbours out."

I opened the bottom of the window and put my head into the bitter night. "Be quiet, Honners. Can't you see the position? What is it you want at this time of night?"

Honners glared up at me in the moonlight. "Oh, so there you are at last, lover boy. You're all right so you don't worry about me. How the devil can I go home when you've got the key of my car? I've been all over town trying to trace you."

Then I remembered how Honners had given me the key so I could borrow his car for the evening, only to find that in this weather there was nowhere to go anyway. "Sorry, Honners. Wait there a second while I fetch it."

I soon located the key in my pocket and returned to the window. Honners called up, "At last! Careful how you throw it down, Peter—we don't want to lose it in the snow after all I've been through. I'll cup my hands, now try and land it in them."

I leaned out as far as possible to aim the key accurately, when suddenly the window-sill moved forward—only it wasn't the window-sill but the thick ice on top of it. I dropped the key in a panic to clutch at the window-frame but this was coated with a rime of frost, so that my fingers slid down its length. Unbelievingly, I found myself gradually sliding out of the window, head first. The experience was so horrible that I clearly remember thinking that I was not so much falling from the bedroom as oozing out like toothpaste from a tube. Honners watched petrified some feet below, his hands still cupped as though he would catch me instead of the key. I shouted for him to jump clear, just as Olga screamed as she saw my feet slowly disappear through the window. Instinctively, Honners dodged aside as I turned a half somersault through the air, but I caught him on the thigh so that he ricocheted out of sight across the tiny garden. I landed silently in the deep snow of the flower-beds, landed on my side with no sensation of pain—merely a feeling of intense cold from the icing-sugar snow that covered me with a tickling featheriness.

"I'm not hurt! I'm not hurt!" I cried joyfully to the sky.

"Well, you're lucky—I'm damned nigh killed! What's more, I've lost my left ear."

It was Honners' voice but I could not see him in the shadow of the fence. My attention was distracted by Olga's white face at the window. "Wait there, Peter, while I dress. Then I'll bring your clothes down," she wailed. "Oh, what a dreadful thing to happen right on my own doorstep."

Even then, it occurred to my dazed brain that if she took as long to dress as usual I might well die of exposure, but to add to the terror of the night, Honners was calling for help.

"Where are you, Honners?" I shouted.

"Over here by the fence. Get help quickly before I die from a broken neck."

"Can't you get up then?"

"How the hell can a poor devil get up when his head's gone through the gate?"

"Can't you pull yourself clear?

"Of course I can't —my head's stuck between the bars of the front gate, just below where it says *No Hawkers, No Circulars*. They're iron bars and I can't shift them. At least I've found my blessed ear, so I'll just have to wait here till you fetch the fire-brigade or whatever fools go about getting people's heads out of railings and suchlike. At the moment I'm resting my chin on the plaque which says *Beware of the Dog*. I suppose my car key's lost for ever."

"Hallo, hallo, hallo—what's going on here, then? You turned nudist or merely gone off your rocker, Pook?"

I stared aghast at the familiar face of Constable Barrington looming over the hedge with the aid of a torch.

"Well, well, well, you've cut some right capers in your time, Pook, but I ain't never seen the likes o' this. Naked we comes into this world and naked we leaves it, eh? Local yob commits suicide in snow, eh? Come clean, lad—is it some new publicity stunt you've dreamed up, eh?"

"Get the fire-brigade fast, you flat-footed slob," Honners yelled angrily. "I'm dying down here on the deck and all you're concerned with is passing the long night with small-talk."

"Ho, ho, is somebody on fire then? That sounded mighty like our little titled toff with the big mouth. Come out wherever you are, Honners."

"I'm down here and if you'll shine that searchlight on the gate you'll see the predicament I'm in. You won't do anything about it, but at least you'll see it."

Constable Barrington went over and examined my friend carefully. At length he said, "My, my, Honners, you've really excelled yourself this time, eh? Your head's well and truly wedged through this 'ere gate."

"Brilliant deduction, Barrington. Until you told me I thought I was playing tennis."

"How come you ain't naked like Pook then?"

"Don't tell me you want me to strip to match?"

"I don't like the look of that ear of yours, Honners. Reckon you'll need a couple of stitches where it joins the 'ead."

"While they're at it they can sew it flat to my skull. I'm fed up with people saying I look like a bat in flight."

Meanwhile I had been banging on Olga's front door, demanding the return of my clothes before I became ill but the sound of female voices inside indicated that Olga and her mother did not see eye to eye in matters of young love. Suddenly the front door came open, my clothes flew out cannon-bag fashion, and the door slammed. Then the row inside continued as before. I waited a minute in case Olga left home at the same velocity, then began to dress as quickly as my numbed hands would permit."

Rejoining Constable Barrington, I found him triumphant in the solution of the immediate problem. Very slowly, lest he break Honners' neck, he lifted the gate off the two lugs on which it swung, then pronounced Honners to be free at last.

"Free!" Honners spluttered, still kneeling in the snow with his head between the bars. "How is a poor devil free when he's still got his head jammed in a kind of Chinese torture cangue? Do you think I can resume my normal place in society carrying a blooming great iron gate about with me? For heaven's sake hold the thing up or it'll snap my head off like a gooseberry."

"Ah, but now we can get you to the hospital, Honners. I'll phone for a squad car."

"Look, mate, how can I possibly get in any car like this? The only possible way is to put me in a lorry—preferably a scrap metal dealer's."

"I see your point, Honners. Oh well, there's only one thing for it and it's not far—we'll just have to walk."

"Walk! I can't even stand up, let alone walk. . . ."

"Never fear, Honners. Pook and me'll take one end each,

with you in the middle. You won't feel any weight at all. Let's get cracking before cockcrow."

Some time or other in our lives we all get caught up in an embarrassing and often ludicrous situation—such as the child whose head becomes wedged in his potty, or the lady whose toe jammed up the bath tap—and tonight reminded me of those accidents which up till now I had only read about in the papers. We presented an odd sight walking along Cudford High Street, Constable Barrington in front, myself in the rear, bearing the gate between us like a stretcher while Honners cursed and moaned in the centre of the little procession—now able to walk upright with his head through the bars, as though caught in some medieval man-trap—pleading with us not to slip on the snowy pavements lest we break his neck.

The few stragglers we passed gazed unbelievingly at the spectacle, laughed and aired their wit on Honners' misfortune. One man, obviously coming from a pub, expressed a hope that tonight's weather would not be stormy, pointing out that Honners was in an unenviable position if struck by lightning.

"Get back up your tree, you drunken anthropoid," Honners snarled savagely.

"First jail-breaker I've ever seen being brought back with his cell window still on him," the man retorted cheerfully.

"Constable Barrington, do your duty for once and arrest that intoxicated bum for slander this instant."

"Then I'll have to drop my end of the gate to do it."

"March on and forget it, idiot!"

Constable Barrington led us straight to the police station, where the duty sergeant stared at Honners calmly as we rested the gate on the counter. "Lost Property received at the far end," he said unsmilingly. "Hold on though; I see you're number 76. Funny, we've just had a phone call from Mrs Brown, 76 Balham Road, reporting her front gate's been stolen. Have you found it or pinched it?"

"Neither, you heartless oaf—I was flung through it when Pook decided to drop on me from the heavens."'

Constable Barrington intervened. "All right, Harry. This is Mrs Brown's gate sure enough but she can't have it back till we've prised Honners out of it. Phone the fire station next door and have them bring over one of their small jacks for bending iron bars they use for freeing kids' heads from railings."

While we waited for the tools to arrive, the sergeant said by way of small-talk, "Now you're here, Honners, there's the little matter of a summons for you."

"Oh, perfect bliss!" Honners groaned wearily. "Is it from the next world gathering me to the arms of my ancestors?"

"No, mate, it's from this world, telling you you ain't got no lights on your car. Your Bentley's been parked all evening in Cudford Crescent without the regulation means of illumination back or front."

"No lights, no key, no hope! While you were at it, did you check the tyres for incorrect pressures and startle the Ministry of Transport by reporting that my number-plates are all muddy? Shall I have to go to prison—reckless criminal that I am?"

"No need to be saucy, Honners, or else we might not be able to get your little neck out of chancery, see? Now, Arthur, what's the charge against Pook?"

Constable Barrington smiled contently. "No formal charge as yet, Harry. Perfectly normal explanation for his conduct. Seems he was having a bit of how's-your-father with a young lady who shall remain nameless, then fell out her bedroom window with joy."'

"You mean to say he was up there with two birds at the same time? Was Joy injured by the fall?"

"No, no, Harry, he fell out the window in his excitement. I found him lying in the snow in a state of extreme undress. What's your excuse for that kind of conduct, Pook?"

"I think I'm engaged," I replied miserably.

"Engaged? Well, all I can say is watch out when you're married to her if there's no snow about. She'll break every bone in your body next time."

"There's a lot to be said for living in a bungalow when you come to think of it."

Honners raised his little head from the counter and gave me his Mafia face. "If ever I get out of this science-fiction mousetrap, Pook, you'll never live to see your wedding."

"Don't be petty, Honners; I had you in mind for best man."

"Or a nice little pageboy wearing a gate round his neck for luck, eh?" Constable Barrington chuckled, savouring the picture. "And Pook struttin' up the aisle in his birthday suit. . . ."

Constable Barrington's flight of fancy was interrupted by the phone, which he answered. "Oh, Mrs Brown, eh? Yes, mam, your gate's here safe and sound, though at the moment Honners is peerin' through it like he's a Peepin' Tom. Yes, Pook's here too. Oh, I see. Yes, I'd feel the same if I was in your shoes, mam. Yes, I'll certainly tell him. Thank you, Mrs Brown, good night." Constable Barrington turned to me with a broad grin of satisfaction. "Set your mind at rest, Pook—you ain't engaged no more."

I smiled for the first time. "You mean I'm free?"

"Not exactly free, Pook—just cheap, as they says. Judging by what Mrs Brown said on the phone about you and Olga, I may soon have the pleasure of taking you into protective custody along o' your little mate Honners."

Just after midnight, Honners sat comfortably in Cudford Hospital to have three stitches put in his ear, enjoying the attention of the nurses who pampered him delightedly. He told them he was Samson just after he had carried off the gates of the city, and referred to the whole incident as Earless in Gaza. They didn't understand the joke but laughed uproariously at whatever he said or did, especially when he asked the surgeon to sew his nose down while he was about it, being fed up with

182

people using it as a coat-hook.

Meanwhile, I was taking my life in my hands outside 76 Balham Road, silently searching through the snow for the key of the Bentley like a thief in the night. I nearly had a stroke when a voice whispered above me, "Here it is, Peter, dear. I found it earlier on. Go quickly before mother hears us. See you tomorrow night as usual—same place. I still love you."

Looking up, I blew a kiss to Olga and hurried off into the night. This, I told myself happily, was only the beginning of my tale of woo.

END

*If you enjoyed reading "Pook's Tender Years",
you can follow more of Pook's adventures in
"Beau Pook Proposes".*

An extract follows.

BEAU POOK PROPOSES

Beau Pook Proposes lays bare the jungle of the used car trade and the ruthless operators standing behind their gleaming bangers. Anything but a woman's world, yet Pook enters it in partnership with his great-aunt Dot, a lady born before the motor car was invented, determined to make good in the nation's toughest mart.

We pity them as the victims of the notorious Tax Man con game, then marvel at Aunt Dot's inspired counter-move against the Robbin' Hoods of auto-ville.

But this story is not all power struggle on the forecourts of Britain. Pook tells of his unrequited love for the beautiful Wanda Wells, and how in his despair he wrote to Nurse Dawn of *Family Help* magazine, and how Nurse Dawn came to his side by return of post to begin a love affair to melt the heart of any franchise dealer—wherein Pook becomes engaged to Nurse Dawn's glamorous sister, Gipsy Rosa with the Crystal Ball.

A poignant novel for all men who love cars and for all women who love ugly, muscle-bound men who love cars.

Pook says beauty is only sin-deep anyway.

BEAU POOK PROPOSES

ONE

My Auntie Dot—or Aunt Dottie as we called her during her more trying phase—was not really my aunt but my great-aunt. She was extremely secretive about her age, always parrying my investigations into our family history by observing that she was born in the year dot or shortly after, having narrowly missed the Flood owing to her mother's delayed pregnancy.

But the fact which held me in awe about her longevity was that her grandmother had danced with the Prince Regent at a ball in celebration of the Battle of Waterloo. Aunt Dot constantly referred to the Prince Regent as Prinny, as if she herself knew him intimately.

"When I was a little girl my Gran often told me how she had danced with Prinny at the Assembly Rooms in Bath," she said, adjusting her indoor hat. Aunt Dot's indoor hat was only a mini-hat, secured by elastic round her bun like a modern party novelty, serving no useful purpose as far as I could see, except to observe the Victorian rule that one always wore some form of head cover, even in bed.

"How much did it cost to get in the Assembly Rooms, Aunt Dot?" I inquired. "It's one-and-sixpence at the Cudford Assembly Rooms." I seemed always to have been a mercenary child. At the early age of three I discovered how adults were taken by my white curls and blue eyes, often patting my head and giving me sweets money. I encouraged such generosity by gazing up at them with the blue eyes stretched beyond their natural aperture, plus a simpering smile that developed into what I imagined to be an engaging chuckle of goo, goo, goo, goo, till a tiny bubble appeared on my lips. I found this most effective, even with strangers at bus stops. If my relations were sitting down I made no bones about it but simply went across and dumped my head on their laps for fondling. Should they not respond I got hold of their hands and placed them on my curly pate, gurgling and bubbling to indicate it was sweetie time.

"One did not pay to enter the Assembly Rooms, Peter," my aunt replied, taking up the local paper to check the Deaths column. "One received an invitation from Beau Brummell."

"Was he the brother of Bo-Peep? Ha, ha, ha, ha!" I laughed to let my aunt know I had cracked another joke. I considered myself an extremely witty child, though often misunderstood by humourless adults. For example, my Headmaster, Dr Windebank, when he pulled me up for a hole in my shirt at school. I promptly told him it was an Airtex shirt, whereupon, instead of laughing inordinately, he took me into his study and caned me for impudence. Likewise in the Royal Marines one Monday morning when I tried to cheer up Sergeant Canyon by pointing out that he had such a long face today that he should have a wheel fitted to his chin. Instead of chuckling he hit me in the mouth and broke a tooth.

Above all, I learned not to joke with girls because they slapped your face and then cried for you. It was most discouraging to make jokes which produced tears from one's audience, like the dreadful night I kissed Hilda Longbothem of the buck teeth. During our love-talk she said she fancied me because I wasn't pretty like Alec, or rich like Stuart, but ugly like the back of a bus. That was why her pet name for me was Number 14, the bus which stopped at her house.

"Hold on very tightly, please, Number 14!" she giggled, so I said she should fit a car bumper round her teeth. She howled so loudly that her father came out to the porch in search of the cat.

As a teenager I knew lots of silly little courting jokes to whisper in a girl's ear, like "Your teeth are like the stars, darling—they come out at night," and "Your eyes are like pools, sweetheart—football pools," and "Your lips are like petals—bicycle pedals," and "Your ears are like shells, honey—artillery shells". Alec supplied me with a new one: "Darling, your tooth is shining in the moonlight," and many more such gems, until it dawned on me why girls kept leaving me to go out with Alec. His success with girls was phenomenal because he had mastered the art of pleasing them by going all sincere and helpless the moment they met, almost as though he had been taken ill.

"Do you think your Gran danced with Bonny Prince Charlie, Aunt Dot?" I asked, not too sure of my time scale.

She looked at me over her Woolworth's reading glasses. "No, Peter, nor did she dance with William the Conqueror. Now try not to disturb me while I read the Deaths."

"Do you know how many people are dead in Cudford Cemetery, Aunt Dot?"

"No, my child."

"All of them. Ha, ha, ha, ha!"

Aunt Dot checked the Deaths every night in the *Echo,* using a candle to reinforce the electric light, as part of her self-imposed duty of keeping the family together, as she phrased it. Our family displayed a great reluctance to being kept together, despite Aunt Dot's efforts, and appeared more eager to break up on every side. I presumed she checked the Deaths so carefully to ensure no member of the family slipped through her net unnoticed, but she also kept tabs on all her contemporaries' families, too—the Nells, Flo's and Ada's, all dearly beloved and sadly missed, whom Aunt Dot had successfully outlived. She invariably read the verses aloud—'One of the best has gone to rest.'—often wiping her eye during a particularly poignant poem recording the final break-up of a marriage by the untimely departure of one of the partners, usually the husband, to the Hereafter to prepare accommodation for his spouse later on.

Aunt Dot was a devout believer in monogamy, that state of married bliss extending to the grave, wherein the husband had no eyes for another woman all his life, worshipping only his wife until she finally extinguished his passion by burying him in Cudford Cemetery.

It symbolized the idyllic, sexless union so dear to the Victorians, from which children, if any, suddenly appeared in group photographs, like waking up and finding a meteorite in your garden.

On the other hand, Aunt Dot allowed herself ardent admirers who followed her faithfully through the years, waiting in vain for their virgin goddess, at first virile young bucks, then tottery old gentlemen, until they too figured in Aunt Dot's favourite column in the *Echo*.

The facts did not quite fit the picture, because Aunt Dot's late husband had had eyes for several women down the years, and Aunt Dot's faithful swains had filled in the waiting period by marrying and re-marrying far beyond the norm of unrequited love. In fact, Aunt Dot's husband, Sydney, spent much of his married life in pubs, which he called refugee camps for husbands, and he was known to be particularly fond of the Bold Forester in Cudford, where women were not encouraged, not only as a customer but also on occasion as a lodger above the tap bar. Sydney made no secret of the fact that he liked war, especially those on the scale of World War I, which he regarded in the light of free foreign holidays for thirty million men unaccompanied by their wives. Rumour alleged that he had gone so far as to petition the Government to start another one shortly before his demise.

Uncle Sydney seldom spoke when not in the Bold Forester, having been born of an over-possessive mother who performed that chore for him whenever he opened his mouth, and this oral function was taken over by Aunt Dot upon marriage. She was able to put his thoughts into words on the basis of an almost telepathic communication between husband and wife, thus: "No, he's had quite enough for one night, thank you, and does not want another drink." Similarly, she was sufficiently clairvoyant to see into the future on his behalf, thus:

"No, Sydney won't be able to play darts tomorrow

night because he wants to take me to the pictures."

Aunt Dot had adapted to the cinema with the ease she had adapted to the motor car and the aeroplane earlier in her life. She liked to see Queen Mary in particular on the screen, and when the Queen waved from her carriage Aunt Dot waved back enthusiastically, crying out: "I remember your Grandmother, Queen Victoria, your Majesty".

Some years later her daughter, Aunt Mabel, refused to watch *Songs of Praise* on television if it was supper-time because she considered it irreverent for the congregation to have to sing and see her eating her supper in front of them. Likewise, when the Dean of St Paul's delivered a sermon I was required to stand in front of the screen while Aunt Mabel sipped her gin. If a play displeased her she always forbade me to switch off or change channels lest the actors should lose their jobs on her account; so we had to endure everything in the name of full employment. During these plays she often warned actors who were in danger of attack from behind, and she was especially prone to exposing actresses who were taking advantage of unwary males or good women.

It would have been easy to mock Aunt Mabel on this score but I reminded myself that she came from an era when there were no cars, television, radio, aeroplanes, pneumatic-drills, motor-bikes or articulated trucks to break the heavenly silence that must have hung over the world since the beginning of time right up to Aunt Mabel's coming-of-age. So I willingly changed chairs with her when Hughie Green persisted in winking at her from the screen, and even fetched bread-crumbs to scatter round the set during visits to Bird Island, and looked under the TV table to ensure that the Saint had not dropped his gun there, and searched beneath her bed before retiring, lest the missing body in the Whodunit had been hidden upstairs during the News.

Hanging on the wall was a fascinating sepia picture of Aunt Dot and Uncle Sydney posed on their wedding day like wax-works. Uncle Sydney stood to attention, except that both arms were positioned akimbo to resemble a two-handled vase, as if Aunt Dot was at liberty to put her own arm through either handle. She had chosen the left handle by hanging a gloved hand through it. Uncle Sydney had been married in military uniform, brass-buttoned and bemedalled, crowned by a pillbox hat and strap above a symmetrically perfect moustache shaped like a coat-hanger, the ensemble supported below on a pair of robust boots, indicative of his determination to march to the honeymoon resort.

Aunt Dot was one huge wedding dress, bustle, train, veil, hat, gloves, bouquet, horseshoe, ribbons, flowers, jewellery, beads, muff, feathers, prayer book, fan, leg-o'-mutton sleeves, frills, curls and several unidentifiable accessories essential to a Victorian bride. She must have had a bottom drawer like a haberdashery warehouse, and Uncle Sydney once told me how Aunt Dot's legs had been designed by nature on the dining-room table principle, solely to keep her body off the floor.

Beneath the wedding-cake hat so little of Aunt Dot's face was visible except nose and mouth that there was scant pictorial evidence to support the theory that Uncle Sydney had married Aunt Dot. It could have been anyone, or even a dummy supplied by the photographer. As a child, I gazed at the picture for hours, trying to solve the mystery of why Aunt Dot had been married in a palace of Imperial Rome. They were posed on the marble steps of some mighty edifice, flanked by statues of Mars and Julius Caesar, leading up to the Temple of Jupiter. Through the fluted columns of the portico I could see the Vestal Virgins performing a dance, while in the extreme background there was a tantalizing glimpse of the Roman Legions fighting the Sabines. Adding to the mystery was the faded caption on the border of the picture : 'Bert Langer & Son, Popular Studios, 27a High Street, Cudford. (Opposite Station.)'

"Were you married during a battle, Aunt Dot?" I inquired puzzledly.

"I certainly was, my child. There was the Boer War in South Africa and your uncle's family on the home front."

"Is that Uncle Sydney's family fighting in the picture?"

"In a manner of speaking, yes, Peter. Or it could be the reception."

"Why did you have a pagan wedding, Aunt Dot?"

"Because I married into a pagan family. Your uncle always thought he was a Centurion in the Imperial Guard instead of a Sergeant in the Hussars."

"Why did you wear your wedding cake on your head, Aunt Dot?"

"It was safer there than at the reception. If you look closely you will see a crate of beer hidden beneath my bridal train for the same reason."

"Why are the bridesmaids dancing in the temple with

no clothes on, Aunt Dot?"

"I expect your uncle had pawned their dresses."

In actual fact, Aunt Dot was anything but pagan, being High Church to a degree. She attended St Mildred's for the purpose of worshipping Father Dee, a worthy cleric whose histrionic personality sometimes relegated God to a side chapel, and who was considered by my aunt to be the English Pope. Today Father Dee is dead and his beautiful church has been prostituted as a warehouse pending its demolition to make room for the modern short-cut to Heaven, a motorway—but his influence and good works live on despite progress and roadworks.

I found it extremely disconcerting to have Aunt Dot praying for me when I started teenage courtship in Cudford. After my first date with Hilda Longbothem she took me aside to her bedroom, where we knelt in prayer while Aunt Dot raised her eyes to the ceiling to ask that I might be given strength for my ordeal. At first I thought what a good idea this was under the circumstances, but I soon realized that the strength I needed was to overcome carnal desires and to despise weaknesses of the flesh, that I might go through life like a lay monk and not see Hilda Longbothem again. I learned to countermand her prayers by silently reversing all her requests, praying to see Hilda Longbothem again as soon as possible, and to be given strength to cope with all the other girls I had my eye on locally. Furthermore, I added a special prayer that Aunt Dot might not find out about them, especially Bunty Tope, who had already offered me sixpence to take her into the back row of the Troxy Cinema.

Soon I was offering thanksgiving prayers in respect of Margaret McKay—my first introduction to the most feminine and desirable of the female species, the Scots lassies. Margaret McKay, with her demure ways, saucy tongue and delightful laughter, rapidly had me praying that my family should move house to Scotland, that I might reside at the source of supply of these irresistible charmers whose Robbie Burns' dialect was for me the language of love.

Learned, too, that life goes full circle, for soon I was praying for strength to overcome carnal desires and reject weaknesses of the flesh in case Margaret McKay wrecked my prospects of becoming a professional footballer by leaving me a burnt-out roué at the age of fifteen.

I remember my Uncle Sydney telling me that the ideal age for marriage was fifty-five, provided your bride was wealthy and in poor health. Uncle Sydney had a most peculiar facial expression difficult to describe in words. It was as though he kept opening a jam-pot and finding a wasp inside which flew out to sting him. Another eccentricity of his was to rise from the meal table for the purpose of emptying the tea-leaves on the carpet, then sweeping the carpet all over with a longhandled broom. This process resulted in a dust-free brown carpet.

Uncle Sydney also arranged daily rows with his wife to keep her happy. He explained to me how women liked rows, and how many marriages broke up for the lack of them. He said that in the past there was no radio, let alone television, so people had rows instead—whereas today people had to be content with watching rows on television, which wasn't the same, just as seeing cookery programmes was no substitute for eating food.

Uncle Sydney explained the three ways to have a row with women. The first was to disagree with what they said; the second was to agree with what they said; the third and easiest method was to say nothing. The most successful husbands said nothing, thus allowing the wife the whole show without the inconvenience of competition or interruption. When Uncle Sydney died, Aunt Dot declared she missed their rows more than any other facet of a long married life.

Another thing Aunt Dot liked was gossip, especially about fast women. A frequent caller was Madam Maude, who went to Paris a lot on unspecified business I could never fathom. As a child I loved to be in the room when she called because Aunt Dot made larger-than-life grimaces behind her back to my relations and mouthed silent words to them, like 'all lies' and 'don't mention Fred'.

When Madam Maude had departed, presumably to Paris, Aunt Dot invariably informed the company that our visitor was too fond of John Thomas, and that her obsession for this individual would prove her undoing. My inquiries as to who John Thomas was always seemed to throw the company into confusion and I was reminded it was past my bed-time.

"If Madam Maude loves John Thomas so much, why does she go to Paris with Uncle Fred?" I asked Aunt Dot puzzledly.

Uncle Sydney looked in his jam-pot, saw a wasp, then exclaimed that I had answered my own question.

"Don't be disgusting, Sydney," Aunt Dot admonished

him. "As for you, Peter, you shouldn't display such unnatural curiosity in what the grown-ups say."

I went over and dumped my curls on her lap to forestall bed-time, then gurgled a bit to bring out her maternal instinct. "Peterkins only wants to know who John Thomas is, Auntie," I whined. "Lots of the ladies talk about him and Madam Maude loves him, yet he never comes here to see us. Isn't Uncle Fred jealous?"

"Don't bother your head with such nonsense, child, and stop calling yourself Peterkins as though you were still a normal infant instead of a precocious little eavesdropper."

"I've even looked him up in Kelly's Directory but I can't find him, so I expect he lives in Paris."

"Here's sixpence for some sweeties tomorrow, so go to bed now and try to dream about puff-puffs and Red Indians like other children of your age."

"How do ladies jump into men's trousers, Auntie?"

"Bed, child!"

"Would Uncle Fred teach me to play slap-and-tickle, Auntie?"

"Off to bed with you!

"Why does Madam Maude always blush when Uncle Fred says that, Auntie?"

Another occasion I shall never forget was Aunt Dot's birthday party when she stood up to make her memorable speech about her great age and how one could live too long on this earth. I recall how the family nodded agreement and said "hear, hear", and my Uncle Ted whispered something about leaving them the money before they were all dead. Then Aunt Dot sat down and disappeared from this earth as I pulled her chair away from under her—a stupid and dangerous prank I still regret to this day. The company was so shocked that brandy had to be administered all round until some members of the family were actually drunk with remorse, and my father patted my head in such a way that I got a fat ear. But they all said I was only six, so I couldn't be held responsible and remarked what a cute, repulsive child I was. My Uncle Ted explained to me what a dreadful thing I had done to my aunt and gave me a shilling.

To compensate for my behaviour I piped up with my little jokes about Aunt Dot being so old that she needed three birthday cakes to hold all the candles, and that if she lived much longer Saint Peter would send down for a doctor's certificate. Everybody laughed and said what a precocious, revolting child I was, to be sure, so I chuckled engagingly and offered my curly head all round for fondling and sweetie money.

When Aunt Dot had taken sufficient brandy to recover from the fall and the family had had enough of my new laugh, which I produced by covering the lower lip with my teeth and going fee-fee-fee-fee-fee for as long as they would stand for it, Uncle Ted inquired what I would be when I grew up.

"Judging by the way he's going on now he'll probably grow up to be an orphan," my father predicted.

"If he grows up," Uncle Sydney warned. "What would you like to be, Peterkins?"

"I should like to be rich," I replied without hesitation. "And I should like to be a money-lender, and I should like to be a lover man like John Thomas."

"It is my opinion," Aunt Dot said coldly, "that if he studies hard he could become a qualified idiot."

"Then you could leave me all your money, Auntie—fee, fee, fee, fee!" I ran round to Aunt Dot and thrust my head on her lap to remind her I was her ultimate heir. To keep the family on their hospitality toes, Aunt Dot let it be known that she had Money, and the family let it be known that they could do with it while still in possession of their faculties. Uncle Ted had gone so far as to give her a pamphlet on how to avoid death duties by an early dispersal of wealth, but I, with the ingenuousness of youth, once confronted her wearing my Dick Turpin mask and brandishing my Dick Turpin cap-pistol to deliver the familiar ultimatum of "Your money or your life!"

Such was the influence of the cinema during my early days that I shocked the family by producing a plan whereby we could obtain our inheritance without detection following Aunt Dot's nightly glass of stout and her resultant departure to the next world with the glass still in her hand. Rich aunts were ten-a-penny in the movies I saw every week at the Troxy, wherein their role was to get knocked off while the audience were settling in their seats and stowing their coats underneath, in order to get the plot going and provide the money for which the principal actors were to murder each other during the rest of the film. We knew from the movies that only bank tellers and Fort Jackson sentries had a shorter life expectancy than rich aunts, their acting careers prematurely terminated by bullets, arrows and arsenic in that order, almost before the house lights had been lowered.

My father was extremely angry when I explained my plan to him, declaring I must be severely punished by being sent to bed early. I tried to cry in case he noticed it was already past my bedtime, and dumped my curly head on his lap.

"Peterkins thought you would be pleased with him for planning something you often said you would do yourself, dad-dah," I whined, getting hold of his hand and putting it on my head.

"I think it is high time you and I had a private talk together, my boy," father said.

"If it's about the birds and the bees again, dad-dah, can we get on to genes and chromosomes, like we're doing at school?"

I attended the Convent of the Holy Angels, where they had to struggle on without the aid of modern educational theories, relying on good tuition and hard work to produce results. I was now eight years old and already studying such subjects as Biology, Algebra, French, Latin and Greek. Despite this old-fashioned approach to learning, we were all happy, normal children without psychological or neurotic complications, nor were we too exhausted to play football, cricket and tennis in our free time.

"No, Peter, I want to talk to you about your obsession with money. Now, your mother gave you a nice teddy-bear money-box some time ago. Have you been using it?"

"Yes, dah-dah. I save my sweetie money and my pocket-money and my presents."

"How can you save your presents?"

"I sell them to my friends, dad-dah."

"So how much is in your money-box to date?"

"Thirty-eight pounds, fourteen and fivepence ha'penny, dad-dah."

"Ye gods!"

Like most adults I spoke to, my father seemed shocked every time I opened my mouth, like at school where most of the boys were studying for the priesthood or missionary work. I was there on a much less positive basis, having derailed a tram with the aid of our kitchen poker, as I described in *Pook's Tender Years*. When Bishop Maloney visited the Convent of the Holy Angels to ask the boys about their careers, he smiled serenely at future priests and missionaries until he came to me. I replied, "Fleet Gunnery Officer, Monseigneur," which seemed to wipe the smile off his face, even though Reverend Mother Blake warned him I was a Protestant.

Bishop Maloney received a second surprise when he crossed over to the girls to see who wanted to be nuns, where he observed pretty little Daphne Coombe my ex-girl-friend, slightly marred today by a black eye she received in a dispute with me over this very vocation of nunhood. Bishop Maloney had a word with Mother Blake, whereupon she told me to open all the windows in the hall owing to the warm weather. While I was performing this chore I noticed that Bishop Maloney was blessing all the other children. I hurried back and knelt down in front of the Bishop with my eyes shut and hands clasped in order to be blessed, but now all the other children were kissing his ring.

Mother Blake came over and told me I could close the windows now because of the draught. I complied as quickly as possible, then joined the kissing queue, but Bishop Maloney was now blessing our rosaries. Being a Protestant I didn't possess a rosary so I pinched Daphne Coombe's and hurried back to the Bishop, only to find he had suddenly begun to bless Mother Blake. I knelt down beside her in blessee pose on her left, just as the Bishop turned to the right to commence a general prayer for all Roman Catholics in the room.

"Bishop Maloney forgot to bless me, Mother Blake," I complained.

"Oh, what a shame, child. Never mind, go and fetch the holy water and he'll do it then."

"Where is the holy water, Mother Blake?"

"In the Chapel of Rest, Peter."

"But that's nearly half a mile away."

"So you must hurry, child, or you'll miss him."

I set off across the Convent grounds for the Chapel of Rest as fast as my little legs would carry me, but when I returned breathless with the jug of holy water I saw all the children singing on the steps of the main building. Mother Blake called out, "Join in the singing, Peter," so I did with gusto.

After three verses I said to Daphne Coombe, "What are we singing for, little nun?"

"We're singing good-bye to Bishop Maloney," she informed me in treble song. "We're singing farewell to his Grace tra-la."

"Where is he then?"

"He's gone back to Ireland far over the sea; Oh, 'tis such a pity he cannot take me, tra-la."

"Sing up, everybody!" Mother Blake cried over our

heads, so I stood there singing as loudly as I could, "We're singing good-bye to Bishop Maloney; We're singing farewell to his Grace, tra-la. He's gone back to Ireland far over the sea; Oh, 'tis such a pity he cannot take me, tra-la."

The high moral tone of the Convent of the Holy Angels was one which did not look with favour on pupils murdering rich aunts for their money, yet it demanded that one told the truth—even if you had murdered her. Thus I was slightly hurt that my father did not believe how much was in my money-box until he had counted it for himself. When he had satisfied himself I had told the truth I made sobbing noises and wiped my eyes with his tie. Then I said, "Dad-dah doubted Peterkins' word, didn't dad-dah?"

"Yes, I'm afraid I did, because I couldn't imagine any child of your age amassing so much money. I'm sorry, Peter. While we're at it, for heaven's sake stop snivelling and calling me dad-dah—my friends at the club wonder if you're mentally retarded or something."

"Shall I call you pah-pah, dad-dah?"

"Call me anything you like but don't drag it out as if you're in pain. Another thing, Peter, you're too old now to go around ramming adults with your head for sweets money."

"Supposing—just supposing—I could save fifty pounds in my money-box by next Christmas, would you double it like Alec's dad-dah does?" I did not add that the sum doubled by Alec's father was seven shillings.

My father laughed at the notion, so I gave him the big blue eyes and pouting lips. "All you need now is a bar of soap and you'd be Bubbles," he chuckled. "Yes, Peter, I'll take you on for fifty pounds provided you don't . . . er . . . well, provided your Aunt Dot isn't involved in any way. You mustn't have bad thoughts about your aunt even in fun, understand?"

"Don't go away, dad-dah, because I have a big surprise for you. I'll run upstairs and fetch it."

Momentarily my father experienced an uneasy feeling that I had gone to drag Aunt Dot's body down to the living-room for his inspection, but I soon reassured him by returning with my china piggy-bank. Opening it I proudly counted out fifteen pounds, three shillings and ninepence, plus odd farthings and foreign coins.

"I've managed to save up fifty-three pounds, eighteen and fourpence, dad-dah," I announced triumphantly, doing the sum in my head, then doubling it. "So now you've made your lovely promise I've got one-hundred-and-seven pounds, sixteen and eightpence—enough to buy a new Ford motor-car and I'm only eight. Aren't I a lucky little shod?"

When my father had recovered from the revelation of my early business acumen he took me to task over what I had called myself. He said, "Where on earth did you pick up that vile expression, Peter?"

"Oh, it's Uncle Sydney's pet name for me," I explained. "He often uses it when he's a wee bit drinky."

"Do you know what it means?"

"I think it's something to do with horses' hoofs, dad-dah."

"Good. We'll leave it at that. Now you come along with me to the Post Office and we'll open a savings account for you. That way you won't lose my money."

"And I'll earn a lot of interest, too, dad-dah."

"Do you know what interest is already, Peter?"

"Principal multiplied by Rate multiplied by Time divided by one hundred equals interest, dad-dah. We learn it at school."

"Remarkable! Could you work out how much interest your hundred pounds will earn?"

"Five pounds, dad-dah."

"No, Peter—two pounds, ten shillings."

"No, dad-dah, five pounds. Auntie Dot has promised to double it for me."

"Now I know why Uncle Sydney called you a lucky little shod. What made her do that?"

"Because I promised not to poison her stout, dad-dah."

As my father donned his hat he gave me a long searching look.

. . . . *Continued in "Beau Pook Proposes", which can be ordered from all good bookshops or direct from Emissary Publishing.*

EASY EXERCISES
FOR THE OLDER PERSON
by
Monica P. File, MCSP

Cover design and illustrations:
William T. File

only £5.50 inc. p.&p.

This book is intended for older people and carers.

It is easy to read and understand, giving beneficial exercises and general tips designed to help older or disabled people to maintain their health and independence.

The author is a chartered physiotherapist with forty years experience.

I wish to order_____copy/copies of *Easy Exercises For The Older Person* by Monica P. File, MCSP at £5.50 each (inc.p.&p.) *(Add £1.00 per book for Overseas Post/Packing; ensure cheque is for sterling and drawn on an English Clearing Bank.)*

Please make cheque/postal order payable to:Emissary Publishing

Total amount enclosed:£_____Date_____

NAME (Block Capitals)_____
ADDRESS(Block Capitals)_____

_____
_____Postcode_____
Tel No. (if poss: in case of query)_____

Please complete coupon (or photocopy) and send with your cheque/postal order to: Emissary Publishing, P.O. Box 33, Bicester, Oxon, OX26 2BU, U.K. *(Or visit our website at www.emissary-publishing.com)*